Do you hear those sounds?
What are they? A fox dreaming? Hands talking?
Sunspots falling? Just listen. They're the sounds of stories.
They may be strange. They can be funny. They're often magical.
You'll hear them all and many more when you read

Cover, Introduction, and Title Page Illustrations by Reg Cartwright. Reprinted by permission of Folio.

Acknowledgments appear on page 231.

Printed in the U.S.A.

ISBN: 0-395-51921-7

DEFGHIJ-VH-9987654321

Just Listen

Senior Author
John J. Pikulski

Senior Coordinating Author
J. David Cooper

Senior Consulting Author
William K. Durr

Coordinating Authors
Kathryn H. Au
M. Jean Greenlaw
Marjorie Y. Lipson
Susan Page
Sheila W. Valencia
Karen K. Wixson

Authors
Rosalinda B. Barrera
Ruth P. Bunyan
Jacqueline L. Chaparro
Jacqueline C. Comas
Alan N. Crawford
Robert L. Hillerich
Timothy G. Johnson
Jana M. Mason
Pamela A. Mason
William E. Nagy
Joseph S. Renzulli
Alfredo Schifini

Senior Advisor
Richard C. Anderson

Advisors
Christopher J. Baker
Charles Peters

HOUGHTON MIFFLIN COMPANY   BOSTON
Atlanta   Dallas   Geneva, Illinois   Palo Alto   Princeton   Toronto

FICTION
9

Family Album

BOOK 1

12 Jam *by Margaret Mahy*

24 Margaret Ziegler Is Horse-Crazy
by Crescent Dragonwagon

42 The Patchwork Quilt
by Valerie Flournoy

POETRY
39 Little *by Dorothy Aldis*

THEME BOOK
The Wednesday Surprise
by Eve Bunting

IT'S MAGIC

BOOK 2

68 The Great Houdini
from the book by Anne Edwards

86 The Floating Princess
from Magicians Do Amazing Things
by Robert Kraske

94 Six Magic Tricks You Can Do
from Now You See It:
Easy Magic for Beginners
by Ray Broekel and Laurence B. White, Jr.

THEME BOOK
More Magic Tricks You Can Do
by Judith Conaway

Signs of Friendship

BOOK 3

110 The Origami Truce
from Lucky Charms & Birthday Wishes
by Christine McDonnell

136 Becky *by Karen Hirsch*

146 Clancy's Coat *by Eve Bunting*

POETRY
132 I Wish *by Beatrice Schenk de Regniers*
134 Together *by Paul Engle*
135 Poem *by Langston Hughes*

THEME BOOK
Lucky Charms & Birthday Wishes
by Christine McDonnell

BEWARE!
TROUBLE AHEAD

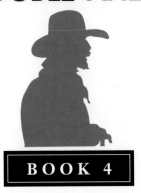

BOOK 4

168 Doctor De Soto *by William Steig*

180 Beware of the Glump
a puppet play by Virginia Bradley

192 The Garden of Abdul Gasazi *by Chris Van Allsburg*

POETRY
210 A Warning About Bears, More About Bears,
Still More About Bears, Last Word About Bears
by John Ciardi
212 The Bloath *by Shel Silverstein*
213 Something is there *by Lilian Moore*

THEME BOOK
Lyle, Lyle, Crocodile *by Bernard Waber*

GLOSSARY
218

FICTION

BOOK 1

FAMILY ALBUM

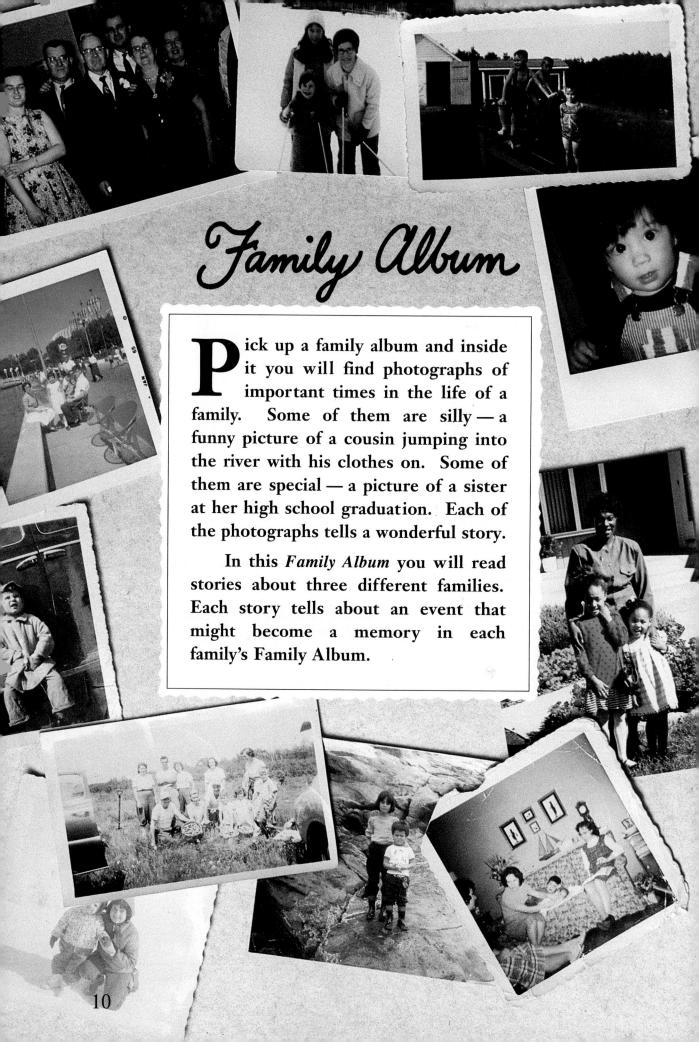

Family Album

Pick up a family album and inside it you will find photographs of important times in the life of a family. Some of them are silly — a funny picture of a cousin jumping into the river with his clothes on. Some of them are special — a picture of a sister at her high school graduation. Each of the photographs tells a wonderful story.

In this *Family Album* you will read stories about three different families. Each story tells about an event that might become a memory in each family's Family Album.

CONTENTS

12
Jam
by Margaret Mahy
with illustrations by Helen Craig

24
Margaret Ziegler Is Horse-Crazy
by Crescent Dragonwagon

42
The Patchwork Quilt
by Valerie Flournoy
with illustrations by Jerry Pinkney

A TRUE STORY

JAM

by Margaret Mahy

with illustrations by Helen Craig

Mr. and Mrs. Castle lived in a white house with a big, green lawn. Their three children were called Clement, Clarissa, and Carlo.

"Three little Castles," said Mr. Castle, "but very small ones — more like Cottages, really."

Mrs. Castle was studying to be an atomic scientist.

"What a clever one *she* is," said Mr. Castle. "If she decided to go to the moon I don't think she'd even need a rocket to get there."

One day Mrs. Castle announced that she had found herself a job. Important scientists were developing an electronic medicine to cure sunspots, and they had sent for Mrs. Castle.

"But who is going to look after us?" asked Clement.

"Isn't anyone going to be here when we come home
from school?" asked Clarissa. Carlo was too young to say
anything, but he looked worried.

"*I* shall be here, my dear little Cottages," Mr. Castle
cried. "You have no reason to be anxious."

He washed and dried the dishes. He vacuumed the carpets, put the dough to rise in a warm place, planted a row of cabbages, folded the wash, baked the bread *and* a cake . . .

He swept the house from top to bottom, wiped down the counter, had a quick cup of tea, put Carlo down for his afternoon sleep . . . had another cup of tea . . . prepared dinner . . .

cleaned the bath . . . read the paper . . . kissed the children when they came home from school — and Mrs. Castle when she came home from work — and asked them all what sort of day they had had.

Then he gave Mrs. Castle something to drink, handed her the paper, and took the children out for a game on the big, green lawn. He was an excellent housefather.

Indeed, he was so good that one day he actually ran out of work. While he tried to think of just what to do next, there came a soft thud on the roof, and then another one.

"Sunspots!" cried Mr. Castle, and ran outside. It was not the sound of falling sunspots he had heard, but ripe plums tumbling off the old plum tree that grew behind the house.

Mr. Castle was delighted. Gathering up the fallen plums he made three pots of plum jam.

"Jam! What a treat!" the children cried.

The next day many more plums fell from the tree and Mr. Castle made twenty pots of plum jam.

The following day the ground under the tree was covered with big, purple plums. That day Mr. Castle had enough plums to make thirty pots of jam.

But the day after that there were even more plums. Mr. Castle had run out of jam jars.

"What a challenge!" he cried. "Not a single plum must be wasted."

He filled all the vases in the house with jam. He filled all the glasses, too. Even Carlo's rabbit mug and the teapot were filled with jam.

"The whole house is like a jam factory," said Clement.

"It's like a school for jam pots," said Clarissa.

"Your father is a born artist," said Mrs. Castle. "He is the Picasso of jam makers."

"Now all the work is done," said Mr. Castle, looking pleased. "We can look forward to eating this delicious jam all year long."

They began with jam sandwiches. Mrs. Castle,
Clement, and Clarissa had jam sandwiches in the lunches
Mr. Castle prepared for them every morning. Carlo, who
was cutting new teeth, had jam on his crusts.

"Hooray!" called Mr. Castle. "We've emptied the
teapot already. We'll be able to have tea with our cakes,
cookies, and tarts."

That winter the roof leaked a little. Mr. Castle's jam
proved very useful, for as well as being delicious, it stopped
leaks. When the tiles came off the bathroom floor, Mr.
Castle stuck them down again with jam. After weeks of
devoted jam eating they could put flowers in the vases
again, and drink from glasses instead of from eggcups.

"I wouldn't really care if I never saw another pot of jam
in my life," Clarissa whispered to Clement. "But don't tell
Daddy I said so."

In the meantime they had jam with everything, and on
everything, and under everything.

Their dreams became haunted with jam. Clement dreamed that the sky opened and jam rained down on him. Clarissa dreamed of fat, shadowy jam pots marching through the night, crying out a terrible war cry of "Jam! Jam! Jam!"

Mrs. Castle dreamed that it was proved that sunspots were caused by too much jam, and Carlo dreamed great jammy dreams as well. Their days were full of jam eating, and their nights of dreams all dripping with jam.

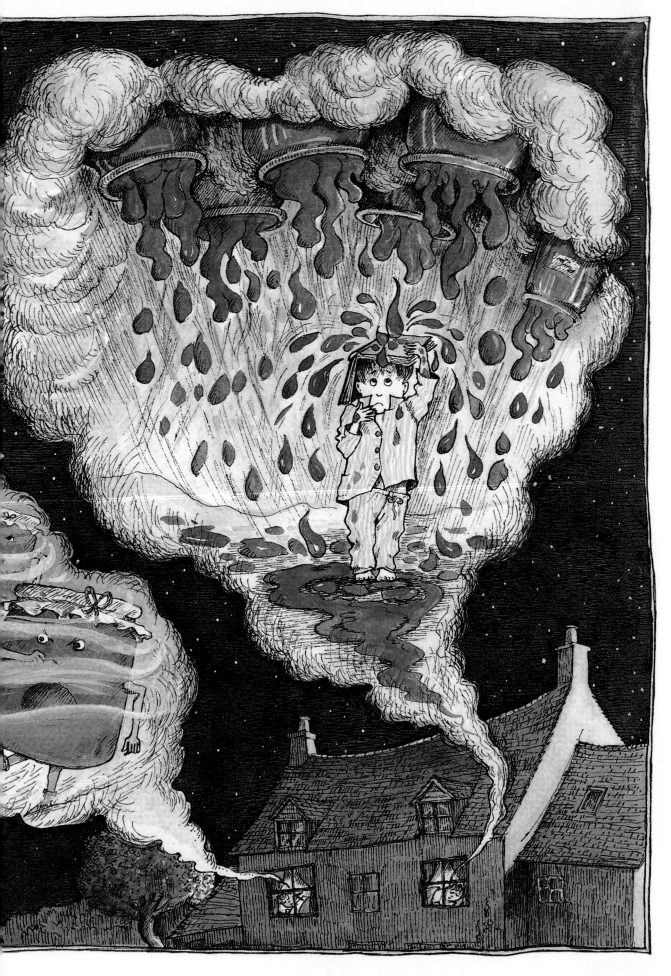

Finally, one morning Mr. Castle went to the cupboard to get down the next pot of jam only to find it was empty. There was not a single potful left.

"Let's have egg sandwiches for lunch," said Mrs. Castle.

"Spaghetti and salad," cried Clarissa.

"Let's have fish and chips," suggested Clement.

"But first let's have a game on the lawn," said Mr. Castle. "We've eaten so much jam that we look like jam pots ourselves. We shall have to get back in shape."

While they were playing on the lawn, Mr. Castle heard a soft thud on the roof.

The plums were ripe again.

101 USES FOR

JAM

With a partner, list the ways
the Castles might use up their next
enormous batch of jam. Illustrate some
of your suggestions. Make a booklet,
and call it something like
"101 Uses for Jam."

Margaret Ziegler

Is

HORSE-CRAZY

by Crescent Dragonwagon

illustrations by Frank Riccio

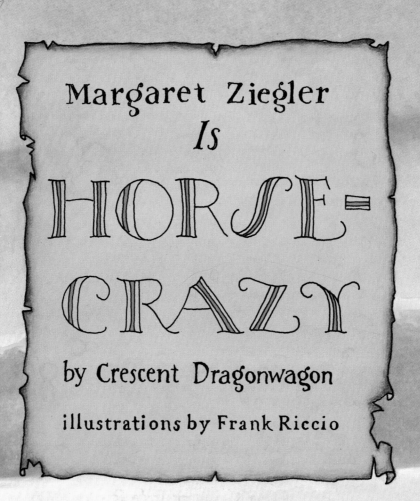

argaret Ziegler is horse-crazy. That's what everybody says. Her mother says it. Her father says it. Her big brother, Rodney, who is always leaving to go to softball practice, says it.

"She's never even been *on* a horse!" says Rodney, snorting.

But Margaret knows better.

It is true she has never ridden on a horse. But soon she will, this summer, at Country Life Riding Day Camp.

Meanwhile, Margaret has a collection of twenty-three horses. Five are made of china, one is made of wood, and seventeen are made of plastic. All of them have names.

"This is Windy, and this is Sundowner, and this is Butterscotch, and this is Luna. . . ."

Meanwhile, she can gallop like a horse. She can also canter, trot, whinny, and neigh, but only when Rodney isn't around. Rodney sniffs and shakes his head. "Not a horse," he says, "but, yeah, you're sure *some* kind of an animal!" He doesn't understand. No one does. They will, though . . . after she begins to ride this summer at Country Life Riding Day Camp.

Meanwhile, Margaret draws horses. She makes a circle for the body above the front legs, and a circle for the body above the back legs, and a smaller circle and an oval for the head. Then she connects the circles, drawing in the neck and back and legs, drawing in a mane flying up and a tail flying out. All the pages of her notebook at school are covered with horses. When her class has Art, she paints a whole field of horses: a red horse, a blue horse, a green horse, a yellow horse, a purple horse.

"Purple horses!" says Rodney. "Boy, she's really gone off the deep end now!"

"Rodney, leave your sister alone," says their mother. "She's just at the age where she's a little horse-crazy."

Rodney shakes his head and asks if he can be excused. He leaves the table, rolling his eyes.

But Margaret doesn't care. When she begins to ride at Country Life Riding Day Camp, they'll see.

Meanwhile, Margaret has a poster of horses up in her room. She studies it.

When her parents' friends, the Sneeds, come to visit, she shows the poster to Mr. and Mrs. Sneed.

"These are the Percherons. They are the work horses," Margaret explains. "These are the Morgans. They are the kind of horse policemen ride. They are very intelligent and loyal."

"That's nice, dear," says Mrs. Sneed. "And now we really have to — "

"This is an Appaloosa," says Margaret. "And this is a pinto, and this is a palomino, and these little ones over here — they are the way horses looked in prehistoric times."

The Sneeds shift from foot to foot.

"Fred? Irene?" calls Margaret's mother.

"Margaret got you trapped up there with her horses?" calls Margaret's father. "C'mon down."

"Thank you for telling us about your horses," says Mrs. Sneed.

"You certainly know a lot about them," says Mr. Sneed.

The Sneeds go downstairs.

From upstairs, Margaret hears her father say, "She's just a little horse-crazy, is all."

She hears her mother say, "She's at that age."

But she'll show them, and soon.

Meanwhile, Margaret wins a prize at school for reading the most books of any child in the third grade. She has read 157 books in one year, all of them about horses. The librarian has had to borrow many of the books from other libraries. "Don't you think you should expand your horizons, dear?" the librarian asks her. In class, Margaret has done book reports on *Misty of Chincoteague, Black Beauty,* and *National Velvet.* But when she does *How to Groom Your First Horse,* her teacher says, "Margaret . . . it's important to be well-rounded."

Well-rounded, thinks Margaret, like a ball, like the stupid softball Rodney is always carrying and tossing and catching in his glove. Hah! thinks Margaret. They won't tell me that after they've seen me ride at Country Life Riding Day Camp.

Sometimes Margaret lies in bed at night, imagining she is grooming a horse. She picks up one foot, carefully cleaning out the dirt around the horseshoe with a hoof pick. Then she does the other three feet. Then she brushes the horse all over with a currycomb. She can almost feel how velvety the horse's smooth neck will be. She can almost feel how much the horse will like being groomed by her.

But mostly what she thinks about is what will happen at Country Life Riding Day Camp.

What will happen, Margaret knows, is this.

Her parents will let her out of the car, and she will walk to a paddock. A big black horse will be in the center of the paddock, rearing up on his back legs and whinnying loudly. "That's Midnight," someone will whisper to Margaret. "He went wild. No one can get near him."

Fearlessly, quickly, before anyone can stop her, Margaret will slip into the pasture. When they see her, everyone will gasp, "Get that child out of there! She could get hurt!" But it will be too late.

"Here, Midnight," Margaret will call softly, and Midnight will stop rearing. He will toss his head once and trot gently over to Margaret, who will pat him on his graceful black neck, on his velvety nose. "Good boy," Margaret will tell Midnight, as she catches his bridle and leads him back toward the stable.

As she passes through the crowd she will hear people whisper, "She has a way with horses." And as she grasps Midnight and pulls herself up onto his back, as they ride away together, she will hear more whispers. "It's a miracle!" "That girl is a natural." "No one's been able to ride that horse for *years*." "She and Midnight are made for each other."

This is what Margaret *knows* will happen at Country Life Riding Day Camp.

But what really happens is this.

At Country Life Riding Day Camp there is a line of twenty-eight girls standing on a ramp waiting for their first riding lesson.

"Attention, please," calls a man holding a clipboard. "I am Mr. Duke. I will call your names and assign you each a horse for today. After I've called your name, stand over there, and Greta, my assistant, will bring your horse out to you. Just stand by your horse, holding the bridle. Don't do anything else till I tell you."

Mr. Duke begins to read the names.

"Barbara Adams — Twinkles." Barbara walks over to the right, where Mr. Duke has pointed.

"Melissa Babcock — Cinnamon." Now Barbara's horse, a chestnut brown mare, is being brought out to her. Barbara takes the reins from Greta as Melissa waits for her horse.

"Clara Chu — Starlight."

"Heidi Erickson — Flame."

"Felice Feinstein — Echo."

As Margaret waits, she realizes to her horror that the names are being called alphabetically. *What if there is no horse left for her?*

But when Mr. Duke reaches *Z,* there is still a horse, one horse, left.

"Margaret Ziegler." He pauses. "Hmmm," he says, "I guess it'll have to be Oleo."

Oleo! What kind of name is *that* for a horse?

Margaret stands at the end of the line of girls, each girl holding her horse.

And she sees Greta pulling on the bridle of a horse who does not want to come.

This horse is white, with big, ugly, brown blotches and
a short, ugly mane that sticks straight up like the bristles
on a toothbrush. This horse is big and fat — much fatter

than any other horse Greta has brought out. Now Margaret knows why this horse, who still doesn't move, is named Oleo.

Greta slaps Oleo on the rump, and finally he moves. She brings him to Margaret. Margaret reaches up and takes him by the bridle. He is certainly big and fat. He is fatter than any horse Margaret has ever even seen a picture of. He is so fat it is scary.

Still Margaret holds the bridle.

Oleo looks down at Margaret. He shows his teeth. He pushes his ears back. He rolls his eyes in disgust.

Now Mr. Duke is coming.

"All right, girls," says Mr. Duke. "First we are going to talk about mounting and dismounting."

At that moment, something awful happens.

Oleo steps on Margaret's foot.

The doctor says that none of Margaret's toes are broken, but they are very badly bruised. He says she shouldn't bear down on that foot for a few days. He advises ice packs.

Margaret hobbles out to the car.

"Here, do you want me to help you?" asks her mother.

"No," says Margaret.

In the car, Margaret's mother says, "Honey, I'm *so* sorry. I know how much you were looking forward to this."

Margaret doesn't say anything. She just looks out the window.

When they get home, Margaret says, "I don't think I want to go back to Country Life Riding Day Camp anymore."

That night, Margaret sits in the big chair in the living room, her foot wrapped up in plastic bags of ice. A blue towel is wrapped around the plastic bags. Her mother is in the kitchen making lemon meringue pie — Margaret's favorite — for dessert, but Margaret doesn't care. Everything is awful.

The front door slams. In comes Rodney, tossing his softball. He looks at her.

"What happened to you?"

Margaret says, "A horse named Oleo stepped on my foot." Then she looks away from Rodney, and big tears begin to roll down her cheeks.

"Hey, great!" says Rodney, kneeling down next to her.

"What do you mean, great?" says Margaret. "Can't you just shut up and leave me alone for once?"

"No, really, I mean it," says Rodney. "It's great! It's your first sports injury. Remember when I got shin splints running track? Remember when I sprained my pitching arm?"

"Well," says Margaret, snuffling, "it may be my first sports injury, but it's also my last. I am never going near another horse for as long as I live. I'm going to take Arts and Crafts at the Youth Center if they still have room. Mom already said I could."

"Well, you *can*, Mags," says Rodney. "But it would be very, very wimpy. You ought to try again. You don't think anybody's perfect the first time they try something, do you?"

Margaret doesn't say anything. Her only consolation is that she has never told her family about Midnight.

"Look," says Rodney, "in all those horse books, didn't it ever say something about how, when you're thrown from a horse, you have to get right back on so you won't get scared?"

"Sure," says Margaret. "But I didn't even get on."

"All the more reason," says Rodney, and he stands up and goes upstairs to change, tossing his softball.

At dinner, Margaret's mother tells Margaret's father what has happened. Margaret's father is very sympathetic. Margaret's mother tells Margaret's father that Margaret has decided to switch to Arts and Crafts at the Youth Center if there's still room. "Of course. Perfectly understandable," says Margaret's father.

"Well, wait," says Margaret. She hasn't said much during dinner. Everyone turns and looks at her. "I've been thinking about it," she says, "and I think maybe I would like to try Country Life Riding Day Camp again. Just try it. When my foot is better. Maybe not every day, but a couple of times a week. And go to Arts and Crafts at the Youth Center the other days, if I could."

"That's my girl," says her mother, smiling.

"Smart thinking," says her father, nodding. "That's a more well-rounded approach, anyway."

"Way to go, Margaret!" says Rodney. "Aw-right!"

Margaret has two pieces of lemon meringue pie for dessert.

JUST CRAZY

Margaret Ziegler was crazy about horses.
What are you crazy about?
Baseball? Computers?
Dinosaurs?

Write about what you like best.
It can be a few sentences or a whole story.
Call it "(*Your name*) Is _____-Crazy."
Share your writing with your group.

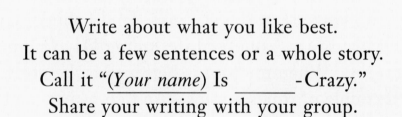

Little

I am the sister of him
And he is my brother.
He is too little for us
To talk to each other.

So every morning I show him
My doll and my book;
But every morning he still is
Too little to look.

Dorothy Aldis

HORSES
OF DIFFERENT COLORS

There are many different kinds of horses. Some plow fields. Some compete in races. Others help cowboys round up cattle.

PALOMINOS
are golden-colored with white manes and tails. They are popular parade horses.

ARABIANS
are beautiful horses known for their strength and endurance.

APPALOOSAS
have spotted coats. They were first used by the Nez Perce Indians.

SHETLAND PONIES

are from a Scottish island and are so small that they were once used in the coal mines of Great Britain.

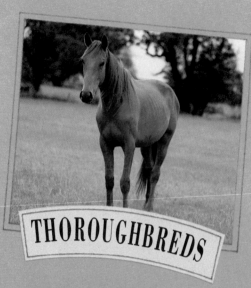

THOROUGHBREDS

are used in horse racing. They are tall and very fast.

MORGANS

are named after Justin Morgan's famous horse, Figure. All Morgans are related to Figure.

CLYDESDALES

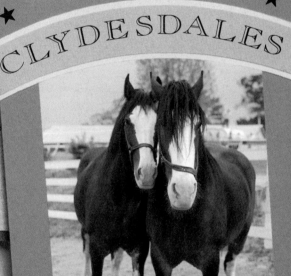

are large horses used to plow fields and pull heavy wagons.

The Patchwork Quilt

Written by
Valerie Flournoy

Illustrated by
Jerry Pinkney

Tanya sat restlessly on her chair by the kitchen window. For several days she had had to stay in bed with a cold. But now Tanya's cold was almost gone. She was anxious to go outside and enjoy the fresh air and the arrival of spring.

"Mama, when can I go outside?" asked Tanya. Mama pulled the tray of biscuits from the oven and placed it on the counter.

"In time," she murmured. "All in good time."

Tanya gazed through the window and saw her two brothers, Ted and Jim, and Papa building the new backyard fence.

"I'm gonna talk to Grandma," she said.

Grandma was sitting in her favorite spot — the big soft chair in front of the picture window. In her lap were scraps of materials of all textures and colors. Tanya recognized some of them. The plaid was from Papa's old work shirt, and the red scraps were from the shirt Ted had torn that winter.

"Whatcha gonna do with all that stuff?" Tanya asked.

"Stuff? These ain't stuff. These little pieces gonna make me a quilt, a patchwork quilt."

Tanya tilted her head. "I know what a quilt is, Grandma. There's one on your bed, but it's old and dirty and Mama can never get it clean."

Grandma sighed. "It ain't dirty, honey. It's worn, the way it's supposed to be."

Grandma flexed her fingers to keep them from stiffening. She sucked in some air and said, "My mother made me a quilt when I wasn't any older than you. But sometimes the old ways are forgotten."

Tanya leaned against the chair and rested her head on her grandmother's shoulder.

Just then Mama walked in with two glasses of milk and some biscuits. Mama looked at the scraps of material that were scattered all over. "Grandma," she said, "I just cleaned this room, and now it's a mess."

"It's not a mess, Mama," Tanya said through a mouthful of biscuit. "It's a quilt."

"A quilt! You don't need these scraps. I can get you a quilt," Mama said.

Grandma looked at her daughter and then turned to her grandchild. "Yes, your mama can get you a quilt from any department store. But it won't be like my patchwork quilt, and it won't last as long either."

Mama looked at Grandma, then picked up Tanya's empty glass and went to make lunch.

Grandma's eyes grew dark and distant. She turned away from Tanya and gazed out the window, absentmindedly rubbing the pieces of material through her fingers.

"Grandma, I'll help you make your quilt," Tanya said.

"Thank you, honey."

"Let's start right now. We'll be finished in no time."

Grandma held Tanya close and patted her head. "It's gonna take quite a while to make this quilt, not a couple of days or a week — not even a month. A good quilt, a masterpiece . . ." Grandma's eyes shone at the thought. "Why I need more material. More gold and blue, some red and green. And I'll need the time to do it right. It'll take me a year at least."

"A year," shouted Tanya. "That's too long. I can't wait that long, Grandma."

Grandma laughed. "A year ain't that long, honey. Makin' this quilt gonna be a joy. Now run along and let Grandma rest." Grandma turned her head toward the sunlight and closed her eyes.

"I'm gonna make a masterpiece," she murmured, clutching a scrap of cloth in her hand, just before she fell asleep.

"We'll have to get you a new pair and use these old ones for rags," Mama said as she hung the last piece of wash on the clothesline one August afternoon.

Jim was miserable. His favorite blue corduroy pants had been held together with patches; now they were beyond repair.

"Bring them here," Grandma said.

Grandma took part of the pant leg and cut a few blue squares. Jim gave her a hug and watched her add his patches to the others.

"A quilt won't forget. It can tell your life story," she said.

The arrival of autumn meant school and Halloween. This year Tanya would be an African princess. She danced around in the long, flowing robes Mama had made from several yards of colorful material. The old bracelets and earrings Tanya had found in a trunk in the attic jingled noisily as she moved. Grandma cut some squares out of the leftover scraps and added Tanya to the quilt too!

The days grew colder but Tanya and her brothers didn't mind. They knew snow wasn't far away. Mama dreaded winter's coming. Every year she would plead with Grandma to move away from the drafty window, but Grandma wouldn't budge.

"Grandma, please," Mama scolded. "You can sit here by the heater."

"I'm not your grandmother, I'm your mother," Grandma said. "And I'm gonna sit here in the Lord's light and make my masterpiece."

It was the end of November when Ted, Jim, and Tanya got their wish. They awoke one morning to find everything in sight covered with snow. Tanya got dressed and flew down the stairs. Ted and Jim, and even Mama and Papa, were already outside.

"I don't like leaving Grandma in that house by herself," Mama said. "I know she's lonely."

Tanya pulled herself out of the snow being careful not to ruin her angel. "Grandma isn't lonely," Tanya said happily. "She and the quilt are telling each other stories."

Mama glanced questioningly at Tanya, "Telling each other stories?"

"Yes, Grandma says a quilt never forgets!"

The family spent the morning and most of the afternoon sledding down the hill. Finally, when they were all numb from the cold, they went inside for hot chocolate and sandwiches.

"I think I'll go sit and talk to Grandma," Mama said.

"Then she can explain to you about our quilt — our very own family quilt," Tanya said.

Mama saw the mischievous glint in her youngest child's eyes.

"Why, I may just have her do that, young lady," Mama said as she walked out of the kitchen.

Tanya leaned over the table to see into the living room. Grandma was hunched over, her eyes close to the fabric as she made tiny stitches. Mama sat at the old woman's feet. Tanya couldn't hear what was said but she knew Grandma was telling Mama all about quilts and how *this* quilt would be very special. Tanya sipped her chocolate slowly, then she saw Mama pick up a piece of fabric, rub it with her fingers, and smile.

From that moment on both women spent their winter evenings working on the quilt. Mama did the sewing while Grandma cut the fabrics and placed the scraps in a pattern of colors. Even while they were cooking and baking all their Christmas specialties during the day, at

night they still worked on the quilt. Only once did Mama
put it aside. She wanted to wear something special
Christmas night, so she bought some gold material and
made a beautiful dress. Tanya knew without asking that
the gold scraps would be in the quilt too.

There was much singing and laughing that Christmas. All Grandma's sons and daughters and nieces and nephews came to pay their respects. The Christmas tree lights shone brightly, filling the room with sparkling colors. Later, when everyone had gone home, Papa said he had never felt so much happiness in the house. And Mama agreed.

When Tanya got downstairs the next morning, she found Papa fixing pancakes.

"Is today a special day too?" asked Jim.

"Where's Mama?" asked Tanya.

"Grandma doesn't feel well this morning," Papa said. "Your mother is with her now till the doctor gets here."

"Will Grandma be all right?" Ted asked.

Papa rubbed his son's head and smiled. "There's nothing for you to worry about. We'll take care of Grandma."

Tanya looked into the living room. There on the back of the big chair rested the patchwork quilt. It was folded neatly, just as Grandma had left it.

"Mother didn't want us to know she wasn't feeling well. She thought it would spoil our Christmas," Mama told them later, her face drawn and tired, her eyes a puffy red. "Now it's up to all of us to be quiet and make her as comfortable as possible." Papa put an arm around Mama's shoulder.

"Can we see Grandma?" Tanya asked.

"No, not tonight," Papa said. "Grandma needs plenty of rest."

It was nearly a week, the day before New Year's, before the children were permitted to see their grandmother. She looked tired and spoke in whispers.

"We miss you, Grandma," Ted said.

"And your muffins and hot chocolate," added Jim. Grandma smiled.

51

"Your quilt misses you too, Grandma," Tanya said. Grandma's smile faded from her lips. Her eyes grew cloudy.

"My masterpiece," Grandma sighed. "It would have been beautiful. Almost half finished." The old woman closed her eyes and turned away from her grandchildren. Papa whispered it was time to leave. Ted, Jim, and Tanya crept from the room.

Tanya walked slowly to where the quilt lay. She had seen Grandma and Mama work on it. Tanya thought real hard. She knew how to cut the scraps, but she wasn't certain of the rest. Just then Tanya felt a hand resting on her shoulder. She looked up and saw Mama.

"Tomorrow," Mama said.

New Year's Day was the beginning. After the dishes were washed and put away, Tanya and Mama examined the quilt.

"You cut more squares, Tanya, while I stitch some patches together," Mama said.

Tanya snipped and trimmed the scraps of material till her hands hurt from the scissors. Mama watched her carefully, making sure the squares were all the same size. The next day was the same as the last. More snipping and cutting. But Mama couldn't always be around to watch Tanya work. Grandma had to be looked after. So Tanya worked by herself. Then one night, as Papa read them stories, Jim walked over and looked at the quilt. In it he saw patches of blue. His blue. Without saying a word Jim picked up the scissors and some scraps and started to make squares. Ted helped Jim put the squares in piles while Mama showed Tanya how to join them.

Every day, as soon as she got home from school, Tanya worked on the quilt. Ted and Jim were too busy with sports, and Mama was looking after Grandma, so Tanya worked alone. But after a few weeks she stopped. Something was wrong — something was missing, Tanya thought. For days the quilt lay on the back of the chair. No one knew why Tanya had stopped working. Tanya would sit and look at the quilt. Finally she knew. Some*thing* wasn't missing. Some*one* was missing from the quilt.

That evening before she went to bed Tanya tiptoed into Grandma's room, a pair of scissors in her hand. She quietly lifted the end of Grandma's old quilt and carefully removed a few squares.

February and March came and went as Mama proudly watched her daughter work on the last few rows of patches. Tanya always found time for the quilt. Grandma had been watching too. The old woman had been getting stronger and stronger as the months passed. Once she was able, Papa would carry Grandma to her chair by the window. "I needs the Lord's light," Grandma said. Then she would sit and hum softly to herself and watch Tanya work.

"Yes, honey, this quilt is nothin' but a joy," Grandma said.

Summer vacation was almost here. One June day Tanya came home to find Grandma working on the quilt again! She had finished sewing the last few squares together; the stuffing was in place, and she was already pinning on the backing.

"Grandma!" Tanya shouted.

Grandma looked up. "Hush, child. It's almost time to do the quilting on these patches. But first I have some special finishing touches. . . ."

The next night Grandma cut the final thread with her teeth. "There. It's done," she said. Mama helped Grandma spread the quilt full length.

Nobody had realized how big it had gotten or how beautiful. Reds, greens, blues, and golds, light shades and dark, blended in and out throughout the quilt.

"It's beautiful," Papa said. He touched the gold patch, looked at Mama, and remembered. Jim remembered too. There was his blue and the red from Ted's shirt. There was Tanya's Halloween costume. And there was Grandma. Even though her patch was old, it fit right in.

They all remembered the past year. They especially remembered Tanya and all her work. So it had been decided. In the right hand corner of the last row of patches was delicately stitched, "For Tanya from your Mama and Grandma."

A Classroom Quilt

The patchwork quilt told the story of a year in the life of Tanya's family. Work with a group of classmates. Make a paper quilt that tells the story of some events that happened in your classroom.

First, fill a large sheet of paper with squares. Next, make patches by drawing or pasting a picture inside each square. When you are finished, hang the "quilt" in your classroom.

SCHOOL BUS

FIRST DAY OF SCHOOL

SCHOOL

Museum
Octob
14

Valentine's Day

SNOW
DECEM
10

Happy Birthday Bobby

Be Mine

Quilts

Yesterday...

In *The Patchwork Quilt*, Tanya's quilt served as an album of family history. Quilts are a tradition in many families. In the past, quilts were a necessity. People used them as bedcovers and blankets. Many of the quilts were sewn with traditional patterns. These patterns had names like "Double Wedding Ring" or "Log Cabin." Other quilts were sewn with original patterns.

"Road to California" was made in Pennsylvania in the year 1900.

58

...and Today

Quilts have many different uses. Some quilts are still used for bedcovers, but many people use them for decoration by hanging them on walls. Other quilts have been made to honor the lives of special people, to celebrate the anniversary of a town, or to raise money for a school project.

▲ "Morning, Noon, and Night" was sewn by the Schoolhouse Quilters Guild of Allegheny County, Maryland. The quilt shows a one-room schoolhouse in the morning, afternoon, evening, and night.

This quilt was sewn by elementary and high school students from across the country. It tells the story of Dr. Martin Luther King, Jr. It is sewn in the "Round the Twist" pattern.

About the Authors

Margaret Mahy

Although Margaret Mahy's stories may seem a bit strange, she claims, "I always write about real life." "Real life" to Mahy may include a batch of jam that completely takes over a household, or as in *The Boy Who Was Followed Home*, a boy who is followed home by a hippopotamus.

Margaret Mahy decided as a child that she wanted to be a writer: "I used to write in little notebooks, which I also illustrated. When I got to the middle of the notebook, I always celebrated by drawing a picture, and if I got tired of the story, I would draw many more pictures, for they took up room. I always thought the stories I wrote should be exactly the same length as the notebook."

Another Margaret Mahy book you might like is *The Man Whose Mother Was a Pirate*, about a man who takes his mother — who once was a pirate — to see the sea one last time.

Crescent Dragonwagon

Crescent Dragonwagon is as crazy about food as Margaret Ziegler is about horses. She has written several cookbooks, and two of her books for younger children — *Alligator Arrived with Apples* and *This Is the Bread I Baked for Ned* —

have to do with food. She gets to try out her recipes at the Dairy Hollow House, a country inn she runs with her husband in Eureka Springs, Arkansas.

As you may have guessed, Crescent Dragonwagon is not the author's real name. The daughter of children's author Charlotte Zolotow, she was originally named Ellen. She chose a new name for herself at age sixteen. She says that if she had known how many times she would have to explain it, she would have chosen "something less flashy."

Valerie Flournoy

Just as the patchwork quilt recorded the happy memories of Tanya's family, Valerie Flournoy's stories record memories of her own life. "All the books I write are somewhat autobiographical," says the author. They reflect events that happened either to Flournoy herself, to a family member, or to a friend.

The Patchwork Quilt, which the author dedicated to her mother and grandmother, grew out of her interest in her own family history and her sadness that she hadn't gotten to know her grandmother better. Another book you might enjoy is *The Twins Strike Back,* which comes from Flournoy's experiences growing up with an identical twin sister.

MORE FAMILY ALBUMS TO FLIP THROUGH

The Wednesday Surprise
by Eve Bunting
Anna and her grandmother are planning a special surprise for her father's birthday. You may be surprised, too, when you find out what it is.

Beans on the Roof
by Betsy Byars
Everyone in the Bean family is trying to write a poem, and the best place to write seems to be the roof of their apartment building.

Vinegar Pancakes and Vanishing Cream
by Bonnie Pryor
Nothing goes right for Martin Elwood Snodgrass. His brother is a sports star and his sister is a brain. How will Martin ever live up to the Snodgrass name?

Fudge
by Charlotte Towner Graeber
Tomas Garcia's Labrador has puppies, and Chad wants one. All Chad has to do is figure out how to take care of a curious, trouble-making puppy.

Elaine, Mary Lewis, and the Frogs
by Heidi Chang
It's a long way from San Francisco to Iowa. Elaine Chow doesn't think she'll ever get used to her new home. Her father, a kite maker, and Mary Lewis, a frog lover, assure her she will.

A Search for Two Bad Mice
by Eleanor Clymer
When her family goes to England, Sarah does not want to leave her cat, Leo. Sarah's sister, Barbara, finds a way to make the vacation fun.

Georgia Music
by Helen V. Griffith
A girl and her grandfather enjoy the summer together on his Georgia farm. A year later things have changed, but the girl finds a way to capture the magic of that special summer.

NONFICTION

BOOK 2

IT'S MAGIC

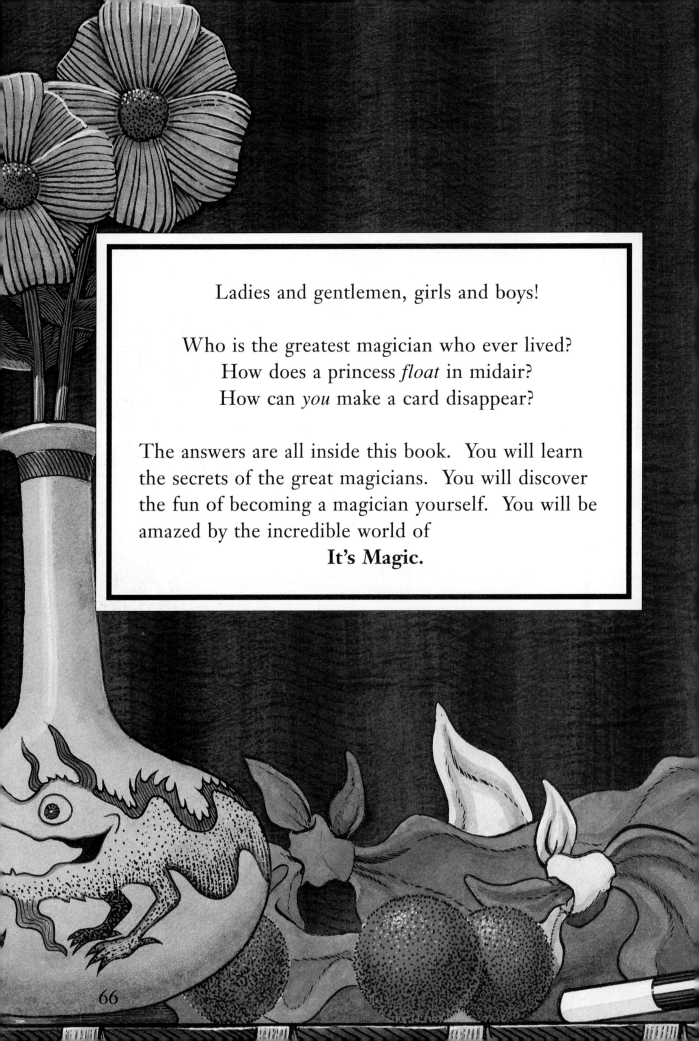

Ladies and gentlemen, girls and boys!

Who is the greatest magician who ever lived?
How does a princess *float* in midair?
How can *you* make a card disappear?

The answers are all inside this book. You will learn
the secrets of the great magicians. You will discover
the fun of becoming a magician yourself. You will be
amazed by the incredible world of
It's Magic.

IT'S MAGIC

Contents

from the book
The Great Houdini 68
by Anne Edwards

The Floating Princess 86
from
Magicians Do Amazing Things
by Robert Kraske

Six Magic Tricks You Can Do 94
from
Now You See It:
Easy Magic for Beginners
by Ray Broekel and
Laurence B. White, Jr.

THE GREAT HOUDINI

from the book
by Anne Edwards

Illustrated by Leslie Holt Morrill

One day Ehrich Weiss would be called Houdini the Great. Now at nine he was already called the Prince of the Air. He swung through the air on a makeshift trapeze rigged to a tree. He wore long red stockings to make him look like a real circus aerialist.

His first performance was in an empty lot which Ehrich, his friends, and his younger brother, Theo, had turned into a circus. Admission was five cents. The boys did not make much money, but Ehrich's daring stunts made the audience applaud. He hung by his feet from the trapeze and picked up things with his teeth. They applauded louder! Ehrich loved the applause. It made him feel special.

Ehrich lived in Milwaukee, Wisconsin. He had been born in Budapest, Hungary, on March 24, 1874, but his parents had moved to the United States when he was a little boy. The five-cent circus was only one of the many things he and his brother did to earn money for his family, who were poor. He worked as a bootblack shining shoes. He sold newspapers on a street corner. Once he and Theo gathered and sold flowers.

A touring magician came to Milwaukee when Ehrich was twelve. His father took the boys to see the man. Ehrich watched the exciting wizard known as Dr. Lynn with amazement. For weeks he tried to figure out the secrets of the magician's tricks. He imagined what it would be like to be a real magician on a stage amazing people.

After seeing Dr. Lynn, Ehrich thought about magic tricks all the time. One snowy December day his family had no money for fuel. Inside the house it was almost as cold as it was outside. Ehrich desperately wanted to do something. Finally, he had an idea.

After work as a delivery boy he stood on the street in the shivery cold with a card pinned to his hat. The snow covered him like a snowman, but everyone could read the card. On it he had printed

CHRISTMAS IS COMING, TURKEYS ARE FAT
PLEASE DROP A QUARTER
IN THE MESSENGER BOY'S HAT.

He had to stand in the falling snow for only an hour. People walking by couldn't help laughing at the funny sight, and being pleased, they all dropped quarters in his hat. Then he raced home through the freezing cold. He stood at the front door and prepared his "trick." When his mother came to the door, he said, "Shake me, I'm magic."

His mother thought Ehrich was being foolish, but she did as he asked. A shower of silver coins dropped from Ehrich's hair, from behind his ears, and from under his coat sleeves. They even came out of his pant legs and the holes in his gloves. His mother had to laugh.

The library near Ehrich's house became his favorite place. He read all the books it had on magic and all the stories about the lives of famous magicians.

After a time he realized there were two things he wanted to do. He wanted to help his family, and he wanted to be a magician. If he became a good magician, he could earn enough money to help.

During the next few years Ehrich worked in a factory cutting neckties, but all he thought about was magic. He would go without lunch to try out his tricks on the other workers.

One book he read over and over again was about a French magician named Jean Eugène Robert-Houdin. He had performed before the French emperor and for Queen Victoria of England. He became Ehrich's hero, and Ehrich dreamed of performing before the queen, too.

Another book he liked was written by Harry Kellar, a famous American magician. Ehrich admired his escape tricks most of all. He would try them out on his brother, Theo, tying Theo up and freeing him in almost no time at all. Ehrich had learned special ways of tying knots which made this possible.

On his seventeenth birthday Ehrich decided to quit his job and go to New York. He would try to find work as a magician, and for this he wanted an exciting new name. He thought about the names of the famous magicians he had read about. Harry Kellar and Robert-Houdin, he said over and over to himself. Finally, he took Harry Kellar's first name and called himself Harry. Then he added an I to Robert-Houdin's last name. He was now HARRY HOUDINI. Theo went with him to New York. They formed an act and called themselves the Brothers Houdini.

Harry and Theo performed wherever they could. Often this was in cafés or at parties and meetings. Sometimes it was onstage at a proper theater with other acts. Once they were hired to appear at the Imperial Music Hall. Harry put Theo into a sack. He put the sack inside a wooden box. Then he locked and tied up the box. Theo had to escape before the audience's eyes. It was a trick the two brothers had rehearsed successfully many times.

Harry called out, "When I clap my hands three times — behold a miracle!"

But this time Theo did not appear.

Harry repeated the command.

No Theo.

The orchestra played louder. The manager brought down the curtain. Harry quickly untied the box. Poor Theo was red and puffing. He had made his way out of the sack through a secret opening. But he had left the key that opened the box from the inside in their dressing room. Harry decided from then on to do his tricks alone.

One day he was riding a streetcar to a performance.
He carried all his magic equipment with him. He had
ropes that looked as if they were one piece but could easily
become two. He had cards that stuck to one another. He
had a magic wand that sprouted flowers and scarves. And
he also had a bottle of clear liquid that turned to red
liquid when it was exposed to the air. The streetcar ride
was a bumpy one. Harry had a difficult time holding onto
the strap and to his box. Then — crash! went the box.
Everything spilled onto the floor. The bottled liquid that
turned red broke. It turned deep red and splashed all over
the skirt of a pretty girl standing next to him. Her dress
was ruined. The girl's name was Bess. Harry took his
paycheck that day and bought Bess a new dress. They
became friends, and this was the girl Harry later married.

Harry and Bess traveled all over the country. She had always been interested in the stage herself and so became his assistant. But Harry did all the tricks. He liked the escape tricks best. Harry studied everything there was to know about locks — how they worked, the different kinds of locks, and how to open them. He discovered that by using a piece of crooked metal, called a pick, he could unlock locks without a key. Once he understood everything there was to know about locks and how they worked, he developed the skill to open a lock or handcuff in minutes without a key. He added new escape tricks with both locks and handcuffs into his act, often staying in the theater after the show was over to work out new tricks.

He would free himself from five pairs of handcuffs and a set of leg irons. He escaped from ten pairs of handcuffs and a strapped and padlocked straitjacket which held his arms tightly to the body so he could not move. Wherever he appeared a big sign read:

HARRY HOUDINI
The King of Handcuffs
The Monarch of Leg Shackles

But Harry wanted to be the greatest escape artist of all times. He had his legs locked in irons. Then he had himself locked into a real prison cell. In less than eight minutes he stood on the outside of his cell free from all the things that bound him. A new sign was made. It read:

HARRY HOUDINI
The King of Handcuffs
The Monarch of Leg Shackles
and
The Undisputed Champion
Jail Breaker!

Audiences loved Harry Houdini. He remembered his hero Robert-Houdin who performed his magic before Queen Victoria. He too wanted to perform before the queen. He went to England, but the elderly queen died before Harry could perform for her. Harry was disappointed.

He traveled to Germany and Italy and France, performing his escape tricks. He became even more famous than Robert-Houdin. Soon everyone was calling him the Great Houdini. After five years of traveling all over the Continent, he and Bess returned to the United States.

Harry discovered that it was not easy being famous. There were some people who said he was not really great. These people challenged him publicly. They would walk right up on the stage when he was performing and say he really hadn't locked the cuffs on his wrists or that the rope was a trick rope. But Harry had now perfected his tricks.

He let these challengers lock his cuffs and tie the ropes themselves. Then he still escaped.

There were also people who tried to imitate his act. Harry was angry about this. He had his own challenge printed in the newspaper. He offered anyone who accepted his challenge a lot of money.

I, HARRY HOUDINI,

DO HEREBY CHALLENGE

ANY PERSON IN THE WORLD

TO DUPLICATE MY RELEASE FROM

CUFFS, IRONS

AND STRAITJACKETS

UNDER TEST CONDITIONS.

THAT IS TO ENTIRELY STRIP,

BE THOROUGHLY SEARCHED,

MOUTH SEWED AND SEALED UP,

MAKING IT IMPOSSIBLE

TO CONCEAL KEYS,

SPRINGS OR LOCK PICKERS,

AND IN THAT STATE ESCAPE....

No one accepted his challenge.

Harry decided he would have to do tricks that were impossible for anyone else to do. He would add his gymnastic and athletic abilities to his act. He was a good swimmer and could stay underwater a long time.

He had a tremendous milk can brought onstage. It was bigger than he was. The can was filled with water. Then his wrists were handcuffed. He was placed inside the can. The water was over his head. His assistant put the top on the can and secured it with six locked padlocks. The audience was told to hold its breath for as long as it could. No one was able to do it for more than thirty seconds, and there was Harry still locked in the can covered with water! The audience was terrified. Some shouted for someone to get an ax and get Harry out. Almost three minutes went by before Harry, smiling and dripping wet, emerged from the can! Never had he received so much applause.

But Harry had to make the trick better.

Not long after he did the same trick again. This time he had the can he was locked in lowered into the river. Still, he got out.

But there were many other kinds of tricks Harry liked to perform. He had seen other magicians perform "vanishing" acts in which they made rabbits and birds disappear. The Great Houdini advertised that he was going to make an elephant vanish. The elephant's name was Jennie. She weighed ten thousand pounds and wore a bright-blue ribbon around her neck. Houdini with fifteen assistants led Jennie into a huge box and closed the door. A few moments later the Great Houdini opened the door to the box. The elephant had "disappeared."

But of all the acts he performed, Harry still liked the escape acts best. These took a great deal of training. Whenever he did a new act, he would train three or four weeks for it. He learned how to hold his breath for long periods of time. He practiced breathing in such a manner that he didn't need air for nearly two hours. He developed his muscles. He could be hit in the stomach without injury. His arms were powerful and able to hold tremendous weights. During one show he slipped and fractured a bone in his ankle. Harry stopped long enough to let a doctor look at it. But he was so strong he went right on with the act.

One day a young man challenged Harry's strength. He wanted to see if Harry could be hit in the stomach without feeling pain. Without warning the young man punched Harry in the stomach before he had time to tighten his incredibly strong stomach muscles. During that night's performance Harry was in a lot of pain, but he refused to tell Bess. They had an engagement in Detroit the following night, and Harry was not going to miss it.

"I won't disappoint my audience," Harry said when a doctor was finally called.

The doctor said he had appendicitis and had to go to the hospital, but this didn't stop Harry. The Great Houdini had a show to do.

The Garrick Theater in Detroit was filled to the last seat. The orchestra played a rousing chorus of "Pomp and Circumstance." The Great Houdini walked onto the stage. He made silver coins vanish in the air. He made them reappear clinking in a swinging crystal box. He made a pretty girl disappear and a blooming rose bush

take her place. He did card tricks, taking cards, it seemed, from the air. He did a trick called the Whirlwind of Colors, pulling hundreds of yards of silk streamers dry from a liquid-filled glass bowl and turning them into flags.

But he was beginning to feel very ill. Although his temperature was 104 degrees, he was determined to finish his act.

And so he did, but when it was over, he collapsed. A few days later he died. The Great Houdini had given his last show. That was in 1926.

So great was Houdini that he is still thought of as the greatest magician and escape artist who ever lived. His name means superstrength.

He was a magician extraordinary. He was the one, the only, the Great Houdini.

THE GREATEST
WHO EVER LIVED?

Many people consider Harry Houdini to be
the greatest magician who ever lived.
Now that you have read about Houdini, do
you agree? Think about this question and
how you would answer it.
Then write a short paragraph telling
whether you agree or disagree.
Be sure to explain your answer.

The FLOATING Princess

from *Magicians Do Amazing Things* by Robert Kraske

Illustrations by Kevin Hawkes

———————◆———————

The poster outside the theater read:

TONIGHT — 8pm
HARRY KELLAR
See the Marvel
of the
Floating Princess

On the poster was a drawing of Kellar. A man and a woman stood looking at it.

"Kellar has a bald head," said the man. "Just like my uncle."

The woman said, "He does not LOOK like a magician. I don't think he could fool anyone."

That is what many people said about Harry Kellar. But Kellar was one of the best magicians of the early 1900's. Another magician once said, "On the stage, Kellar does miracles!"

"The Floating Princess" was one of his very special "miracles."

People in the theater saw a young woman on the stage. She was lying on a sofa. She wore the costume of a princess from India. Her name was Princess Karnac.

". . . nine . . . eight . . . seven . . . six . . . " Kellar slowly counted as he hypnotized the princess. "You are falling into a deep sleep. Five . . . four . . . three . . . two . . . one. . . . Now you are sleeping . . . sleeping . . . a deep . . . deep . . . sleep. . . . "

Kellar turned to the people.

"Ladies and gentlemen. For hundreds of years, magicians in India have made people float in mid-air. After years of travel and study, I, Harry Kellar, have discovered the great secret. Watch!"

Kellar stepped over to the woman on the sofa. He waved his hands above her.

"Up!" he commanded.

For a moment, nothing happened. Princess Karnac stayed on the sofa. Then slowly she began to rise . . . up . . . up. Soon she was six feet in the air.

Kellar pulled away the sofa. There was nothing under the princess.

"Impossible!" people said. "She is floating in mid-air!"

A helper gave Kellar a large hoop about five feet wide. Kellar showed it to people in the first row.

"Please feel the hoop," he said. "Is it one piece? Make sure there are no spaces in it."

The people felt it. They looked at it closely. "Yes," they said. "The hoop is all in one piece."

"Then watch!" Kellar said.

Kellar went to the floating princess.

He placed the hoop over her head. Slowly he walked to her feet. The hoop passed along the woman's body. Then he walked the hoop back to her head.

Kellar then placed the hoop over the woman's feet.
He walked it up to her head. The people saw the hoop
pass again along her body. NOTHING WAS HOLDING
HER UP!

Kellar gave the hoop to his helper. He pulled the sofa
back under the princess.

He held up his hands. Slowly he lowered them.
Gently, the woman floated down . . . down. . . . Then she
rested on the sofa. Kellar clapped his hands once . . .
twice . . . three times. The princess blinked. She sat up.

Kellar turned to the people and bowed. They clapped
and cheered. They were amazed at what they had seen. A
woman floating in mid-air!

Did Kellar perform a miracle? Did he really make the
princess float in mid-air? What is your guess?

How Kellar Did It

Did you say that "The Floating Princess" was a clever trick? You were right. Onstage beside Kellar, you would have seen how the trick worked.

The woman was really lying on a board on the sofa. Her hair and dress covered it. A black iron bar went from the board through an opening in the curtain. The audience could not see the bar.

A helper stood behind the curtain. When Kellar said "Up!" the helper pulled a rope. The rope went over a wheel above the helper's head. Then it went down to the bar. The helper's pull lifted the bar, the board, and the princess. It looked as if she were floating in the air.

How could the hoop go along the woman's body?

The iron bar was bent in a long S curve. When Kellar moved the hoop from the woman's head to her feet, the hoop went into one curve of the S.

When he came to her feet, Kellar stopped. He could not move the hoop farther. Next he moved the hoop back to her head. He took it off and walked to her feet. There he placed the hoop around her feet and walked it to her head. The hoop went into the other curve of the S.

The audience thought the hoop passed all along the princess. But it didn't.

Was Princess Karnac a real princess? No. She was one of Kellar's helpers. Was she hypnotized? Not at all. She enjoyed a little rest.

With "The Floating Princess," the old "uncle" who didn't look like a magician fooled everyone. Did he fool YOU?

Write a speech introducing Harry Kellar's magic show.
Make the show seem exciting and mysterious.
Once you have written the speech, practice saying it.
Then present it to your class
as if they were actually going to see
the great Harry Kellar himself.

Before You Turn the Page

Most of the tricks you are about to
read take no time at all to learn. It is still
a good idea to practice them by yourself
before doing them for an audience.
This will give you confidence.

♥

Confidence Is a Magician's Best Friend.

If you mess up a trick, don't feel
discouraged. Laugh about it
or make a joke. Say something like this:
"Some day I'll get this trick right.
When I do, it won't be a trick.
It will be a **miracle**."

Six Magic Tricks You Can Do
from the book

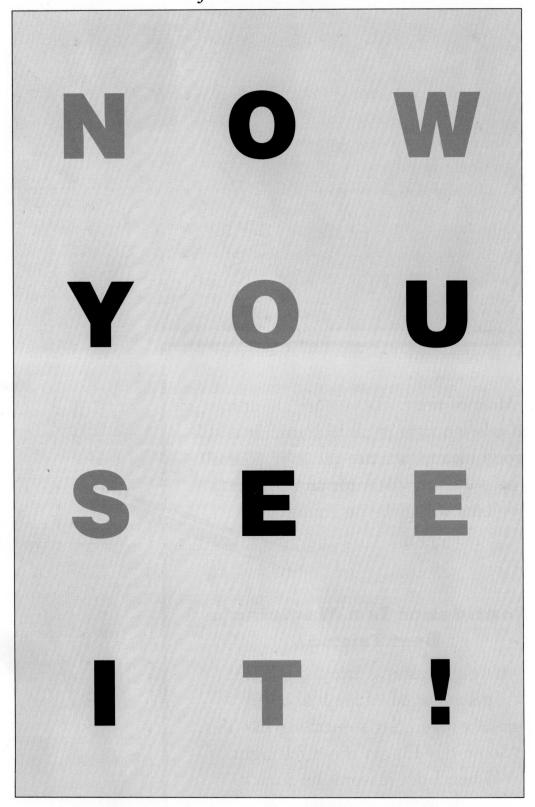

Easy Magic for Beginners

by Ray Broekel and Laurence B. White, Jr.
Illustrations by Steve Lindblom

1. The Balancing Straw

You'll need a plastic straw for this trick.

Place one end on your fingertip. The straw balances! It seems impossible. Everyone knows a straw balances only at its middle. But you balance it from one end.

Now hand the straw to a friend. When your friend tries to balance it, the straw falls. No one but you can do it.

How Is It Done?

2. Fun with Your Thumb

You toss a handkerchief over your hand. Your thumb pokes up underneath. A friend takes hold of your thumb through the cloth. "Hold tight," you say. Then you walk away. Your friend is left holding your thumb!

How Is It Done?

How Is It Done?

Find a nail without a head. Slip it into one end of a straw. This makes that end heavy. The heavy end balances on your finger.

Tip the straw before you hand it to a friend. Secretly slip the nail out into your hand. Now the trick won't work. Your friend doesn't know about the secret nail! (Drop it into your pocket when nobody is watching.)

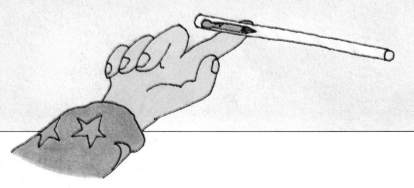

How Is It Done?

This trick will be a big surprise. Nobody expects you to walk away leaving your thumb behind you.

You will need a raw carrot for the trick. Cut a piece off just about the size and shape of your thumb. Hide this in your hand.

Cover your hand with a handkerchief. Poke up the carrot. It will look like your thumb.

Ask someone to hold "your thumb" tightly. When that person does, take your hand away, hiding your thumb in your fist. Then you walk away as the person holds on to the carrot!

③ The Balancing Card

Give your friend one playing card. Ask him to balance it on the table. Tell him it must balance *on one edge*. He tries, but the card falls. It falls every time he tries. Finally he will give up. Now you take the card. Presto! You do it the very first time.

How Is It Done?

④ Your Card Will Disappear

Ask a person to pick a card and remember it. Then place it back onto the deck, face down. You shuffle and mix the deck. "What was your card?" you ask.

The person names it. You say, "I will make that card disappear."

The cards are spread face up on the table. The card the person picked cannot be found. You have made it vanish!

How Is It Done?

How Is It Done?

You use a little trick. That's what a magician must do once in a while. Just before you set the card down you fix it in a certain way.

Here's how. Bend the card a little in the middle. The bend makes it balance easily!

How Is It Done?

Soap! Soap is your secret helper. Put a little dab of bar soap on the back of the top card in the deck. Have your friend choose a card from the middle. You have him put his card on top of the deck. Right on top of the soap card.

Make sure the two cards line up exactly. Now squeeze the deck. This makes the picked card stick to the soaped card.

Mix the deck and spread it face up on the table. The picked card will not be found. It is secretly stuck to the back of the soaped card.

SOAP

⑤ The Rising Cards

You show a deck of cards and a paper cup. You place the cards in the cup, and hold the cup on your hand. You say, "Rise, card." A card slowly rises out of the deck. You say, "Rise, card," again. Another card mysteriously rises!

How Is It Done?

⑥ Ice Water

Pour a little water into a paper cup. Say you will make the water disappear. Ask someone to hold out a hand. Pour the cup into it.

The person expects to get wet. An ICE CUBE falls out instead. Say that you tried to make the water disappear — but it was too HARD!

How Is It Done?

How Is It Done?

Find a paper cup that just holds a deck of cards. It must be a *paper* cup. Why? Because you must cut a hole in the bottom.

As you hold the cup, poke your middle finger up inside. Make sure nobody sees this finger. It is your finger that makes the cards rise. Just push them up from the back of the deck.

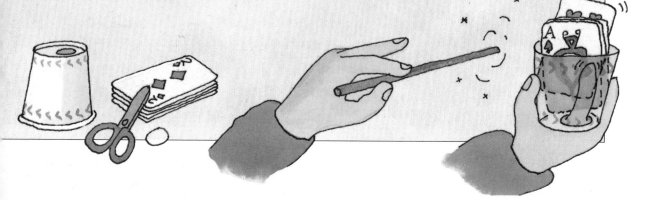

How Is It Done?

This trick is very easy to do. You will need a piece of dry sponge. Cut it into a round shape so that it fits into your cup. Glue it to the bottom.

Put an ice cube into the cup. Have another cup of water handy. Now you are ready. Pour a little water into the cup. (The sponge soaks it right up.) Pour the ice cube out onto someone's hand. What a surprise!

TRICK NOTEBOOK

Now that you have read about a number of magic tricks, make a notebook of some of your favorites. You can include the tricks of Harry Kellar and Houdini as well as some of the tricks in this selection. You might also include tricks from other magic books.

Describe how each trick is done and include drawings, if you wish.

MEET THE AUTHORS

Anne Edwards

Anne Edwards began her career as a movie and television writer in Hollywood. She is the author of many books; this is her second book for children.

Robert Kraske

Robert Kraske has spent many years writing magazine articles and books for children. He has written about Harry Houdini and other famous daredevils, life in outer space, pirates, the Statue of Liberty, and many other topics.

Ray Broekel

One of Ray Broekel's favorite hobbies is magic. He enjoys doing magic tricks and uses them when he talks to elementary schoolchildren about writing. With Laurence B. White, Jr., he wrote many easy magic books for beginners. He has also written books for children about sports, science, and careers.

Laurence B. White, Jr.

Laurence B. White, Jr., says he "caught the magic bug" in first grade. As a child, he took magic lessons from a local magician. While in college, he earned money doing magic shows. As an author, White is especially interested in sharing his love of magic with children. Look through his books, and you may catch the magic bug too!

Reading Is Magic

More Magic Tricks You Can Do
by Judith Conaway

Each trick in this book begins with a poem and shows some magic to do in your home.

Soap Bubble Magic
by Seymour Simon

Soap bubbles can be magical. Try some of these simple experiments. See if you can hold a soap bubble in your hand.

The Mickey Mouse Magic Book
by Walt Disney Productions

First, make a magic wand. Next, say the magic words. Now you are ready to make a penny appear and to do other great tricks.

Magic Mirror Tricks
by Marion Walter

Discover the magic of mirrors. Read this book and learn the many magic tricks you can perform with just a mirror.

FICTION

BOOK 3

Signs
of
Friendship

What are signs of
friendship? An unexpected
gift or kindness. A shared
giggle and a pillow fight.
A little tea and a lot
of forgiveness.

Signs of friendship are
everywhere, even though
sometimes they are hard to
see. The characters in this
book learn to find these
special signs. Read these
stories and you too will
discover signs
of friendship.

CONTENTS

110 **The Origami Truce**
from **Lucky Charms & Birthday Wishes**
by Christine McDonnell

136 **Becky**
by Karen Hirsch

146 **Clancy's Coat**
by Eve Bunting

The Origami Truce

by Christine McDonnell
illustrated by Joyce Audy Zarins
and Ginny Joyner

Every day in September at recess Emily and Ivy liked to play games with the small pink balls you could buy at the candy store, the ones called high bouncers. Their friends played, too.

"A my name is Alice and my husband's name is Arthur and we live in Alabama and we sell anteaters."

Phyllis bounced the ball in a steady rhythm, swinging her leg over every time she said an A word. Then she went on to the B's.

"B my name is Barbara and my husband's name is Bill and we live in Boston and we sell barracudas." She was trying to think of an animal for every letter in the alphabet.

Emily stood next to Patricia O'Hare, waiting for her turn. Phyllis missed on the letter E. She couldn't think of an E place.

"Egypt," suggested Emily. She always knew E because that was the letter that her own name began with.

The next one up was Patricia. Her bushy curls bounced in rhythm with the ball. She went through the letters quickly. But at J she couldn't think of something to sell. She gave the ball an angry bounce before she tossed it to Emily.

Emily had got up to the letter G when something hard hit her on the back of her neck, making her miss her next bounce.

She rubbed her neck where it stung and looked around. Not far from the circle of girls stood Johnny Ringer, grinning.

"What's the matter, Mott? Can't even bounce a ball?"

"I was doing fine until you came along."

Johnny laughed. "Made you miss, huh?"

"Yeah, you made me miss."

"See. You're not perfect, after all."

"I never said I was."

"Think you're so smart. Showoff."

Emily felt herself blush. Johnny wasn't being fair. She wasn't a showoff.

"Get lost, Ringer," said Ivy. "Find a cliff and jump off."

"Yeah," said Patricia. "You think you're so tough."

"Johnny is a je-rk, Johnny is a je-rk," Phyllis chanted.

Emily didn't say anything. She looked down at the playground and kicked a pebble away. It was probably the same pebble that Johnny had thrown.

"Ah, what do you know, anyway?" said Johnny. He sauntered off with his hands in his pockets, trying to walk like a tough guy.

From that point on, Johnny Ringer picked on Emily at least twice a week. He put paste on her chair. He stole her spelling notebook and hid it behind the hamster cage. He wrote on her desk with a marker, and it wouldn't wash off.

"I don't get it," Ivy said. "What did you ever do to him?"

Emily shrugged. She didn't know.

Finally Leo took Johnny aside. "Listen, Ringer, you're acting dumb. Emily hasn't done anything to you."

"How do you know?"

"Name one thing she's done."

"She gives me a pain. She thinks she's so smart, always winning the math relays and stuff."

Leo shook his head. "That's dumb."

"Don't call me dumb. I'm sick of people calling me that."

"Okay. But listen. Leave Emily alone."

"What'll you do if I don't?"

"You'll find out," said Leo in a low voice.

Johnny looked at him carefully but said nothing. Then, with a quick dart of his fist, he punched Leo in the arm and stepped away fast.

Leo rubbed his arm and went back to his desk.

Emily looked up.

"What a jerk," Leo said, still rubbing his arm. "He doesn't like you because you're smart, Emily."

Emily brushed her bangs out of her eyes and straightened her glasses. "What?"

"That's what he said." Leo made a silly face, as if to try to cheer her up.

Emily looked across the room. Johnny stood by the hamster cage, poking his pencil between the bars.

After that, Emily tried to keep a distance between herself and Johnny. She sat far away from him at lunch and at singing. She wasn't in his reading group, and she hoped she'd never be paired with him in math. At recess she stuck with the other kids, figuring that he wouldn't bother her if she was part of a group.

Ivy tried to cheer her up. "Maybe he'll find someone else to pick on. Maybe he'll catch chicken pox or get the flu and stay out of school for a month. Maybe he'll move away."

Her ideas made Emily smile, but inside she was still worried.

Emily even tried to hide being smart a little. She stopped raising her hand when she knew the answer, and sometimes she made mistakes on purpose when she was at the blackboard.

"Emily, that isn't like you," said Mrs. Higgenbottom. "What's the matter, dear?"

She looked so concerned that Emily almost blurted out the whole problem. But she stopped herself just in time. What could Mrs. Higgenbottom do about it, anyway? Besides, if Johnny found out, he might do something terrible. So she didn't tell Mrs. Higgenbottom, after all.

One day at the beginning of October Mrs. Higgenbottom told the class, "We're having a visitor with us for a few weeks, a teacher from another country. His name is Mr. Uchida, and he's from Japan."

Everyone began to talk at once.
"Can he speak English?"
"What does he look like?"
"What do they eat in Japan?"
"When's he coming?"
The questions blurred together in a hubbub.

"Class, simmer down. I'll answer your questions one at a time."

Mrs. Higgenbottom showed them where Japan was on the globe, and she propped a big map of Japan against the board. The class spent the rest of the afternoon making lists of questions to ask Mr. Uchida.

He arrived on Monday. He had gray hair and a very soft voice. He showed them slides of his town and of the children at the school where he taught.

Every day the class learned something new about Japan. Sometimes they pushed all the desks away and sat on straw mats. They practiced eating with chopsticks, and they learned Japanese words.

Emily was disappointed by some of the things that Mr. Uchida told them. Japanese cities looked a lot like American cities — big, modern, and crowded. People wore the same kinds of clothes as they did in America — suits and dresses and even blue jeans.

117

"But there are some things that are very different,"
Mr. Uchida assured them, and he showed them colorful
kimonos and wooden clogs. He taught them how to draw
with black sumi ink and brushes, and how to write short
poems called haiku. You had to count the syllables, five in
the first line, then seven, then five in the last line. Each
poem was like a puzzle; you had to search for the
right-size words.

Emily wrote a haiku about Johnny:

Like a big mean dog
he chases me all around
biting at my heels.

Then she tried another:

Is he really mad
because I know the answers,
or is he jealous?

She wrote haiku about Leo and Ivy:

He's a funny clown
who wears a smile and a joke.
My friend cheers me up.

She's a bouncing ball.
She likes to talk, laugh, and play.
She sticks up for me.

Emily had so much fun writing haiku that she didn't
worry about Johnny for a while. But when Mr. Uchida
put her haiku up on the board with her sumi ink pictures,
she saw Johnny glare at her again.

After Mr. Uchida had been with the class for two weeks, he arrived one afternoon with a basket full of colored paper.

"Today we will begin to learn origami, the art of paper folding."

One by one, he held up tiny figures of birds and animals made out of paper. There was a penguin, a frog, and a crane that even flapped its wings.

Everyone got several sheets of paper. Emily picked green, blue, yellow, and a deep rose. Ivy picked pink and purple, black and brown.

"I want to make a bear," she said.

Mr. Uchida taught them how to make the first basic folds. Then he gave out instruction sheets for three easy figures — a house, a boat, and a cup.

The first person to finish all three was Johnny Ringer. Mr. Uchida examined his figures.

"Very well done," he said, and pinned them up on the bulletin board. "You may take a more difficult sheet now. You will use the same basic folds, but the figure is more complicated. Follow the directions carefully."

Johnny picked out the penguin sheet. He made the figure out of black paper. Mr. Uchida showed him how to turn the corners into flippers, and how to shape the head and the bill. Johnny's penguin came out perfectly on the very first try.

"You are very good at this, my friend," Mr. Uchida complimented Johnny. "Let me see your hands."

Johnny held out his hands cautiously. He wasn't sure what Mr. Uchida was looking for. Both hands were grimy, with dirt under the fingernails and around the knuckles. There were spots of ink and red marker, but Mr. Uchida didn't seem to notice.

"Look how long and tapered your fingers are. You have very smart fingers, Johnny."

Johnny looked down at his hands, admiring them.

Mr. Uchida patted him on the shoulder. "Take care of those hands. They are a sign of special talent."

Johnny blushed. For once he had nothing to say. He just smiled quietly and picked another sheet.

From then on, Johnny was the expert at origami. His figures were always the best. His folds were straight. He was careful and patient. He moved quickly but never hurried. Soon he became Mr. Uchida's helper, showing the others how to turn a fold inside out, or how to line up the edges exactly. The bulletin board was covered with Johnny's paper animals.

Emily was just no good at origami. She couldn't get the folds right. She couldn't line up the corners, and she couldn't understand the instructions. Her little figures were wrinkled and dirty from the sweat of her fingers. The harder she tried, the more frustrated she became. But she wouldn't give up. She wanted to learn how to make the crane, the graceful little figure that could flap its wings.

She tried and tried. Once, when she looked up, Johnny was watching her. He wasn't laughing. He looked as if he knew just how she felt. Emily quickly looked down at her work again. She felt stupid and clumsy. On purpose, she crumpled a sheet of origami paper into a ball and threw it angrily on the floor. The next time she picked a fresh sheet of paper, Johnny came over to her desk.

He showed her how to line up the corners before making the folds.

"Go slow. Don't rush," he said.

His fingers moved smoothly. Emily followed him, step by step.

"Now I get it!" she said.

Johnny left her on her own, and she finished making the frog and started on the penguin.

That afternoon when she caught Johnny's eye on the playground, he smiled at her instead of glaring or making a face. She waved back.

Soon it was the last week of Mr. Uchida's visit. Emily tried to work up to doing the crane. She got stuck on the bear for a day, and she still had a hard time making the long diamond shape that was the base for the crane.

"I'll never get it done," she complained to Ivy.

"So? You can keep on trying after he leaves."

"No. We'll go on to something new. I know it. It's now or never."

She kept on trying.

On Thursday Mr. Uchida wasn't at school.

"This gives us a chance to get ready for Mr. Uchida's good-bye party tomorrow. We have all day to prepare our surprise," said Mrs. Higgenbottom. "What should we make for him?"

"Let's make good-bye cards with sumi ink," said Ivy.

"And write haiku," said Emily.

"Let's make him a paper kimono to wear at the party," suggested Mary Louise. "We can paint it with birds and flowers to make it look like silk."

Emily looked across the room. Everyone was talking and making plans. Everyone except Johnny. He sat by himself in the reading corner staring out the window.

Poor Johnny, Emily thought. He's going to miss Mr. Uchida. She sat for a while chewing on her pencil and thinking. Then she raised her hand.

Mrs. Higgenbottom nodded. "What is it, Emily?"

"I think we should decorate the room with origami. All different colors.

We can hang them on strings,
lots of them, by the windows
and in front of the boards
and from the lights, too."

"Hey, that'll look great,"
Ivy said.

Mrs. Higgenbottom agreed.
"Good idea. But who will make
them all? We haven't much time."

"Johnny!" shouted the class.

Johnny looked up, surprised.

"How about it, Ringer?" called Leo.

"Okay," said Johnny. "I guess I can do it."

They spent the day preparing for the party. Emily
wrote haiku. Ivy drew pictures. Leo and Phyllis practiced
a puppet show. Mary Louise and Patricia worked on the
kimono. And Johnny sat by the window and made origami
figures. The class stopped their projects after lunch to
learn a Japanese song, and they each wrote a letter to a
child in Mr. Uchida's class in Japan.

"I hope they write back," said Leo.

Johnny wrote an extra letter. The envelope said, "To
Mr. Uchida." Emily noticed it when she put her letter in
the box.

"Want some help hanging up your animals?" Emily
asked Johnny.

He nodded. "But be careful not to bend them."

They strung the figures across the boards and hung
them in front of the windows. The wind turned them
gently on their threads.

"They look like they're flying," Emily said.

They finished just before the bell rang for the end of school. The room was cleared, with desks pushed against the back wall. The floor was covered with mats, and a few pillows from the reading corner were set out.

"Tomorrow everyone should bring in a pillow to sit on. And remember to take off your shoes outside the room," Mrs. Higgenbottom reminded them. "And, Johnny, be sure to be here a little early. You'll be the class host for the day because you've been Mr. Uchida's special assistant."

Johnny stood up very straight and nodded.

The party on Friday was a great success. Mr. Uchida smiled and clapped at everything. He laughed at the play, admired the paintings, and read every poem out loud.

"My students will enjoy getting your letters, and they will write to you in return, I promise."

When it was time to leave, Mr. Uchida put his arm around Johnny.

"Good-bye, special assistant. You've been a big help. Don't forget to take care of those hands, and write to me sometime."

Johnny nodded, but he couldn't smile.

Mr. Uchida seemed to understand. He gave him a pat on the head.

Mr. Uchida left after lunch, and the class put the room back in order. Emily watched Johnny carefully take down his little origami figures. He still looked sad.

I wonder what he's going to do with all those, she thought. She wanted to ask him, but she was a little bit afraid. She remembered how he used to tease her.

But that had been before Mr. Uchida came.

Trying to feel brave, Emily went over to the board where Johnny was working.

"Johnny?"

He looked up.

"What are you going to do with your little animals?"

He shrugged.

"I was wondering." She paused, then started again. "I was hoping that maybe you'd give me one of your cranes. I never managed to make one, and I really wanted to. I could use yours for a model."

A big smile spread across Johnny's face. "Sure. I'll pick you out the best."

As the bell rang that afternoon, Johnny gave Emily a perfect crane made out of deep blue paper. He left quickly. She only had time to say, "Thanks," as he disappeared out the door.

She examined the little figure carefully. Each fold was perfect. She could imagine it flying over the water. She was about to tuck it between the pages of her library book for safekeeping on the trip home when she noticed some writing on the underside of the wings.

She turned it over and read the tiny printing: "For Emily from your friend, Johnny."

She put it carefully in her library book. Then she took one of her haiku and sumi ink paintings from her desk, and on the back she wrote, "For Johnny from your friend, Emily." She put it carefully inside Johnny's desk.

Then she whistled happily all the way home.

You may enjoy reading more about Emily, Johnny, and their classmates in the rest of *Lucky Charms & Birthday Wishes.*

DEAR PEN PAL . . .

Mrs. Higgenbottom's class wrote letters to Mr. Uchida's students in Japan. Imagine that you are in Emily and Johnny's class. Write a letter to a pen pal telling what happened between Emily and Johnny during Mr. Uchida's visit. Be sure to describe how Mr. Uchida and his origami lessons helped Emily and Johnny become friends.

Poems of Friendship

I Wish

I wish I had not told my friend
I'd never speak to her again
and please to go away
and stay away
forever.

That was on the way to school
this morning.
Now it's afternoon
and very soon
school will be out.
I shall be walking home
alone
feeling very very friendless.
Oh! The day seems endless, endless . . .

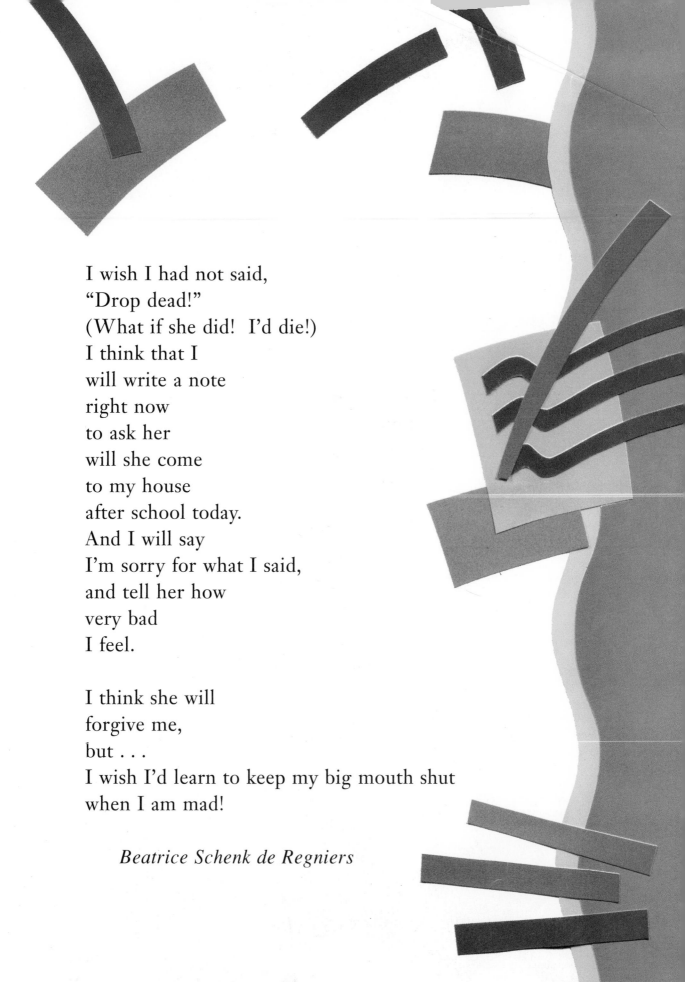

I wish I had not said,
"Drop dead!"
(What if she did! I'd die!)
I think that I
will write a note
right now
to ask her
will she come
to my house
after school today.
And I will say
I'm sorry for what I said,
and tell her how
very bad
I feel.

I think she will
forgive me,
but . . .
I wish I'd learn to keep my big mouth shut
when I am mad!

Beatrice Schenk de Regniers

Together

Because we do
All things together
All things improve,
Even weather.

Our daily meat
And bread taste better,
Trees are greener,
Rain is wetter.

Paul Engle

Poem

I loved my friend.
He went away from me.
There's nothing more to say.
The poem ends,
Soft as it began —
I loved my friend.

Langston Hughes

BECKY

BECKY

by Karen Hirsch ✦ *illustrated by Renée Graef*

ecky can't hear. When she was a baby she had a sickness that made her deaf. Even with her hearing aid, Becky can hear only big, loud noises. She can't hear our voices at all.

Becky is my part-time sister. She lives with our family from Monday until Friday so she can go to school. She has a real mom and dad and brothers and sisters, and she lives with them when it's not schooltime. They live on a farm.

It was a long time ago when I found out that Becky was coming to stay with us. I didn't like it.

"Why does she have to stay here, Mom?" I asked. "I don't want a kid here who I don't even know."

"I read a newspaper article about the hearing impaired program," my mom answered. "It said that homes were needed for the out-of-town children, and we have an extra room." She gave me a little hug. "Don't worry. You'll get to know her."

I wasn't so sure. That extra room had been my brother's and my playroom. Now they made it into a bedroom for Becky. Neither of us liked that. And how could I get to know her? She was deaf.

I was surprised when I first saw Becky. That was two years ago. I guess I thought she'd look different from other people. But there she was, in her jeans and tee-shirt and long ponytails, looking like anyone else.

It was in August, and she came with her parents to meet our family. She was scared at first. I was too. But after her mom and dad and my mom and dad had visited awhile, Becky and I started looking at each other. I couldn't believe that she was deaf. I walked across the room.

"Want to play?" I asked.

She didn't answer. She looked right at me and smiled a little. But she didn't say anything. I felt so strange. I didn't know what to do. So I just left the room.

Becky moved in the day before school opened. She came in a car with her mom and dad and five of her brothers and sisters. They all helped carry in Becky's things. I watched from the garage.

Becky didn't smile at all. Her big brother tickled her a couple of times, and her little sister gave her a licorice candy. They all hugged her and kissed her good-bye. But Becky just stood there, hardly moving.

I found a frisbee on the woodpile and took it outside.

"Want to play?" I asked. I held the frisbee up so she'd understand.

We played frisbee for a while. Then I found my stilts and helped Becky walk on them. She got the hang of it right away. She went all the way down the driveway and back before she fell off.

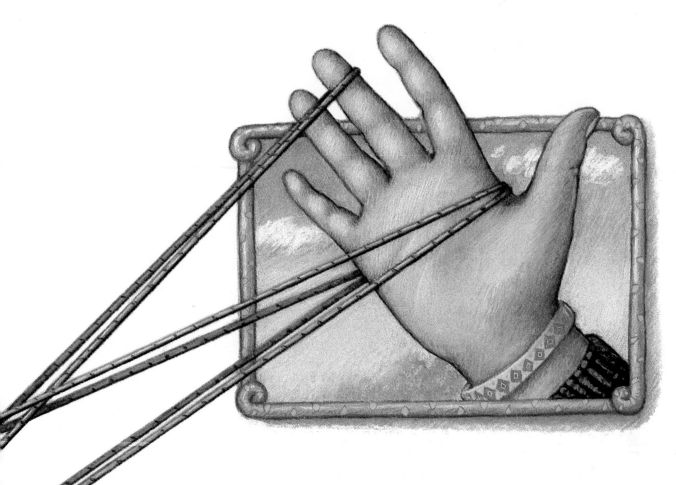

Then she looked right at me and smiled. She reached into her jacket pocket and pulled out a strong string tied into a long loop. She put the string around her hands and started flipping it every which way. She ended up with the string crossed and zigzagged in a pretty design. I'd never seen anything like it.

Then Becky took the string off and handed me the loop. She grinned and pointed at the string and at me. I wanted to try it, but I didn't know how. I shrugged my shoulders. Becky put the string on my hands and showed me what to do.

Most of the time it was really nice having Becky around. Especially on rainy days. Then we painted pictures or did gymnastics. Sometimes we made puppets or helped my dad make chocolate cake. We played the string game, too. Becky showed me a bunch of designs. Some we did together.

"It's called Cat's Cradle," my mom said when I told her about the game Becky had taught me. "It's an old, old game, and all of the designs have names."

The one thing we had trouble with was talking. Then Becky began to learn sign language in school. She learned to talk with her hands. She began to spell out words, letter by letter, and she also learned to sign whole words at a time. My mom and dad took a class to learn sign language and they taught me. That helped because then we could talk to Becky.

Becky also began learning to read lips. We looked right at her and talked in words and sign language at the same time.

Sometimes after school Becky played kickball and foursquare with me and my friends. It went okay usually, but sometimes I got mad at Becky.

When the rules to a game were hard and I couldn't explain them in signs, Becky cried and wanted to play anyway. My friends got mad then, too. "Get her out of the game," they said. "She's goofing it up."

"Go home to Mom," I signed to Becky.

"No!" she signed back. "I want to play!" She cried harder. I took her home then, or Mom heard the fight and came and got her.

Since Becky can't hear, she can't hear her own voice either. She makes loud noises sometimes. But she doesn't know she's doing it.

One day we were at the library — my dad, Becky, and I. Becky saw a man on crutches, and she was so curious she began to point and sign.

"The man is hurt?" she signed. Then she made loud squealing sounds. People all over the library stared. It didn't help to say "Shhh," because Becky didn't know she was making sounds.

My dad explained to the man, and we left. We talked about it in the car.

"There's more she wants to say," my dad said. "She feels upset that she doesn't know all the words she needs yet."

Another time Becky was angry because she couldn't make us understand something at a shopping center.

"I want to go see the — " she signed, and then she stopped. She didn't know the sign for the next word, or maybe she couldn't spell it. She cried and squealed.

"The pet shop?" my mom signed.

"NO!" Becky signed.

"The ice cream shop?" my mom asked in sign language.

"NO!" Becky signed. She cried again and wouldn't let my mom near her.

A man was watching. "Look at that bratty, spoiled kid," he said to his son. That made me mad.

"She is not bratty," I said. "She can't hear. That's all." The man's face got red and he hurried away.

Later these things didn't happen so often because Becky's signing got better and better. Besides, we got used to it too. It was just part of Becky.

One night my mom and I had an argument over my piano lessons. School had just started, so Becky was back with us. My horrible piano lessons were starting the next day. I tried and tried to tell my mom that I didn't want to play the piano. She wouldn't even discuss it, she said. I had to take lessons at least one more year. A half hour of practice a day, she said.

I didn't want to cry, but I got so mad that I couldn't help it. Then I felt someone touch my shoulder. It was Becky.

"Let's go upstairs," she signed. She put her arm over my shoulder. We went to her room and I cried awhile. It was nice to have Becky with me.

A little while after that Becky and I decided to change her bedroom back into a playroom and have my room be a bedroom for both of us. Then we had more fun together.

When we had pillow fights, Mom told us to stop it. It was funny to see her yelling at us in sign language!

Becky will be with us for only one more month. It'll be summer then and she'll go home. Next fall she'll be going to a boarding school for deaf children. I felt sad when I heard about that. Dad told me just last week when Becky and I were helping him wash the car.

"Why can't she stay here and keep going to this school?" I asked.

My dad handed Becky and me the bucket of soapy water and a rag. "Her parents believe that she'll get a better education there," he explained. "But don't worry. We'll always be friends with Becky."

"But Becky's almost my sister!" I said.

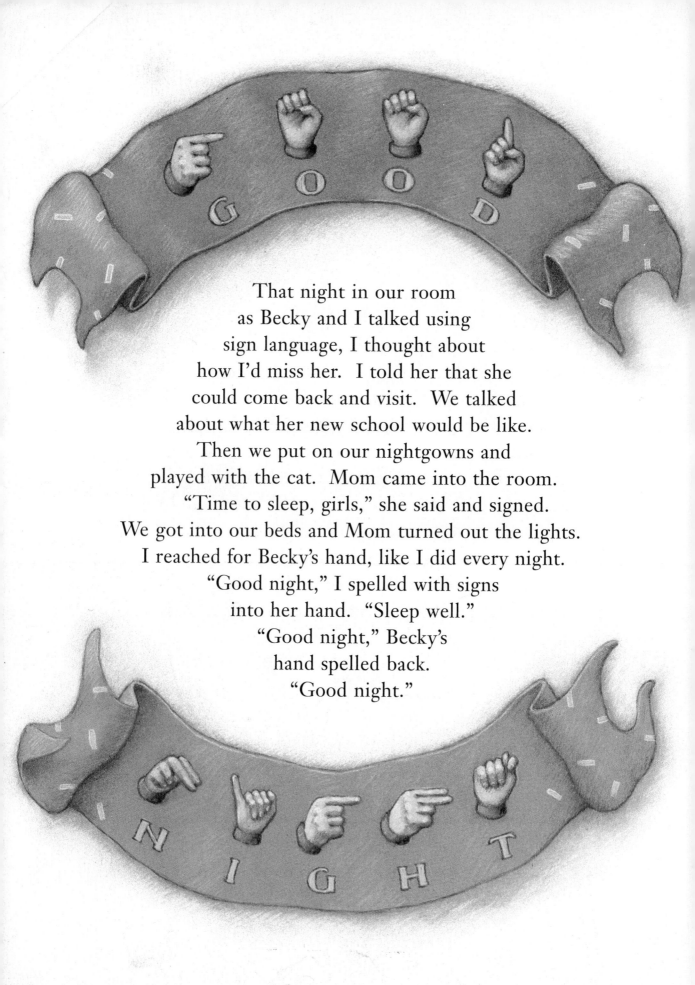

That night in our room
as Becky and I talked using
sign language, I thought about
how I'd miss her. I told her that she
could come back and visit. We talked
about what her new school would be like.
Then we put on our nightgowns and
played with the cat. Mom came into the room.
"Time to sleep, girls," she said and signed.
We got into our beds and Mom turned out the lights.
I reached for Becky's hand, like I did every night.
"Good night," I spelled with signs
into her hand. "Sleep well."
"Good night," Becky's
hand spelled back.
"Good night."

A SCRAPBOOK

Make a scrapbook for Becky to take with her when she leaves to go to her new school. Think of things she might like to remember, like painting pictures, baking a chocolate cake, and having pillow fights. Then make drawings or cut out pictures from old magazines to make Becky's scrapbook. If you like, add a few words to go with your drawings and pictures.

FOR BECKY

EVE BUNTING

Clancy's Coat

ILLUSTRATIONS BY LORINDA BRYAN CAULEY

Tippitt the tailor was having his morning tea when he looked out the window and saw Clancy coming along the road.

"Well, I'll be jakered," he said to Sam, his sheepdog. Hadn't old Clancy sworn never to look in Tippitt's direction again? Hadn't he insulted Tippitt, and Tippitt's good cow, Bridget, too, just because Bridget forgot her manners one day and got into Clancy's vegetable garden?

"Here comes trouble, Sam," Tippitt said, shading his eyes from the sun. "We'll wait for it at the door, for there's no sense inviting trouble into your house."

It wasn't till Clancy got closer that Tippitt saw he was carrying a parcel.

"I've brought you work to do," Clancy said, stopping in front of them. "And I've brought it for the reason that you're the best tailor in Crossgar, and not for the sake of old friendships. Though we were the best of friends and the best of neighbors once, in the days before your cow destroyed my garden."

Tippitt stepped aside and so did Sam. "If it's work you need done you'd better come in."

"I'll come in, then, but I'll not be staying."

"And who asked you to stay?" Tippitt pushed away the teapot and made room on the table for the parcel.

Clancy undid the string and pulled out an old, black coat, shiny with time and wear. Sam cringed back from the smell of mothballs.

"There's a lot of use left in this old coat," Clancy said. "It was a fine piece of cloth and it just needs turning." He pulled one of the sleeves out to show the red wool lining.

"What I need is for you to make the inside be the outside and the outside be the inside, if you get my meaning."

Tippitt raised his eyebrows. "Surely. The coat needs turning."

"That's it." Clancy hung it on the back of a chair and rubbed his hands together. "Powerful cold out." He eyed the brown teapot with the steam rising from its spout.

Tippitt made no move to take another mug from the dresser. "You said you wouldn't be staying."

"Right," Clancy said. "When will the coat be ready?"

"By Saturday."

"I'll be here for it."

Tippitt and Sam watched Clancy go. "It was a sorry day when Bridget got in his vegetables," Tippitt said. "He's a great man for his growing things. It comes from having neither chick nor child to call his own."

Sam nodded, the way he always did when Tippitt talked to him.

"Though my own children's grown and my wife is gone I still have you, my good cow, and my wee hen. All he has are his cabbages and turnips. It's not much, when all's said and done."

Sam nodded again and Tippitt examined the coat. "It'll be as easy to do as skimming cream," he said. "And it'll be done for Saturday."

It would have been, too, except that the night was extra cold, and in the middle of it Tippitt heard Bridget mooing in the barn. When he got up and looked for something to put round her to keep her warm, there was

Clancy's coat. Tippitt took it out, spread it over the cow, and forgot all about it till the next Saturday when he was having dinner and looked out to see Clancy heading up the road.

"Jakers!" Tippitt said to Sam. "Didn't I forget all about Clancy's coat! We'd better invite him to stay a while this time, for he'll be powerful annoyed and in need of soothing."

"Come in, come in," he called from the open door as Sam nodded and wagged his tail.

Clancy took off his muffler and set it on the dresser.

"I see you're eating your dinner," he said. "I'll not keep you, for I only came for my old coat."

"It's not ready yet," Tippitt said. "It's been over my . . . over . . . overlooked. But . . ."

"Moo . . . oooo!" Bridget called from the barn.

"I'll have it for you for certain sure by next Saturday," Tippitt said quickly. "Would you have a cup of tea before you go?" He poured it from the pot, thick as tar and black as night.

"You always did make a good cup of tea." Clancy sat down at the table and eyed the remains of Tippitt's dinner. "Watery looking potatoes you have there. I'm thinking you bought those from O'Donnell of the Glen?"

"Aye," Tippitt said. "And they're like candle grease."

Clancy finished his tea and stood up. "I'll be back for the coat on Saturday."

When he opened the door the March wind came in. "I'll be glad of that old coat," Clancy said, winding his muffler tight round his neck. "There's a lot of use in it yet."

Sam and Tippitt watched till he got all the way to his own wee house down the road, and then Tippitt went to the barn and got the coat from where Bridget was lying on it. And a hard job she made of it, for she didn't want to give it up.

Tippitt shook the hairs from it and set it next to his sewing machine. "I'll start on you in the morning," he told it. And he would have.

Only, that night the wind came up with a terrible fierceness and it blew the whole back window out of Tippitt's house, waking him from a sound sleep. In his hurry to find something to keep out the cold Tippitt saw the coat. He tacked it up where the glass had been and forgot all about it.

The next Saturday Clancy knocked at the door.

"Jakers save us!" Tippitt told Sam. "And the coat's not ready yet! This will take some quick thinking."

He pulled the best chair close to the fire and plumped out the cushions, and he and Sam were both smiling as they met Clancy at the door.

"Come in, sit down," Tippitt invited. "The coat's not fixed yet. It's been in my . . . in my . . . in my mind since I saw you last. But it'll be done by next Saturday for certain sure."

Tippitt noticed that Clancy had a sack slung over his shoulder. "What's this?" he asked.

"Potatoes," Clancy said. "I have them going to waste and I can't stand to see anybody eating poison like the ones you were eating last week. Not even you, Tippitt."

"Well, I'm much obliged." Tippitt decided to ignore the last part of the speech. "Will you have a cup of tea and a piece of my fresh baked bread before you go?"

He sliced a piece, spread it with butter, and carried it to where Clancy had seated himself in the best chair with its plumped up cushions.

"You always did have the whitest bread and the sweetest butter," Clancy said. "I can't buy the likes of it anywhere."

"It's Bridget's good buttermilk that goes into the both of them," Tippitt told him, and wished he'd been quiet because mention of Bridget might remind Clancy and set him off on another uproar.

But Clancy only said: "It's the care you give her. It shows up in what she gives back. Same as me and my garden."

Jakers, Tippitt thought, here it comes. But no more came.

"Saturday, then," Clancy said as he was leaving and Tippitt and Sam both nodded.

As soon as he'd gone Tippitt got the coat from the back window and nailed a piece of wood in its place. He put the coat on top of his sewing machine. "Don't be going any place else," he scolded it. "I'm getting to you tomorrow."

And he would have. Except that the very next day he remembered that he'd promised Rosie O'Brien her skirt for the Friday dance, so he threw Clancy's coat into the corner till he had time to get at it, and Mary, his hen, came right in and set herself on it. And the first thing Tippitt heard was her clucking and panting and swishing her feathers to get herself comfortable before laying her eggs.

Tippitt scratched his head. "Jakers, Sam! It wouldn't be decent to move Mary, and her in the middle of her business. We'll just have to put Clancy off again and we'll have to be smart about it."

On Saturday Tippitt moved his old sofa so that it hid Mary and the coat. He wrapped a big square of yellow butter and set it and a fresh brown loaf in the middle of the table.

"Och, the coat's not finished yet, Clance," he said when Clancy arrived and before he could ask.

"But there's good work being done on it, I'll promise you that."

Then he pointed to the butter and the bread. "I've a couple of wee presents for you here."

"It's a long time since you called me 'Clance'," Clancy said gruffly. He set another sack on the table. "Here's a cabbage for you, and a bundle of leeks and carrots." His eyes slid away from Tippitt's and Tippitt knew he was wishing he'd never said 'garden' the week before just as Tippitt had wished he'd never said 'cow'.

They had tea together, sitting one on each side of the table, the fire flickering and the wee room as warm as toast. Tippitt asked about Clancy's bad leg and Clancy enquired about Tippitt's niece, the one who was married to a policeman and living in America.

154

"It's almost like old times," Clancy said as he got up to leave. "And I'll be back next week for the coat, for there's a lot of use left in it yet."

Mary rustled behind the sofa and went "Cluck, cluck."

"This time, by jakers, he'll have it," Tippitt told Sam as soon as Clancy had gone. "Get a move on there with your business, Mary."

When the chicks were hatched Tippitt gently moved them and thanked Mary kindly for her trouble. Then he carried the coat outside and spread it to air on the hawthorne hedge.

But when he went to take it in he saw that a pair of sparrows were building a nest right in the middle of it.

Tippitt scratched his head. "Well, there's not a soul with a drop of kindness that would disturb a pair of lovebirds when they're building their nest. Should we tell Clance what's going on with his coat, or should we try putting him off another time? I'll admit to something, Sam. I like having Clance around again. And I noticed the way his hands touched those carrots and leeks he brought over. He loves them, so he does. I should have tried harder to know how he felt when poor Bridget stepped all over his garden."

Sam nodded.

"You think I should tell him where the coat is, then?"

Sam nodded again.

When Clancy came he brought a bunch of new rhubarb, pink and tender.

"Isn't that the loveliest thing?" Tippitt said. "And inside there's some of Bridget's good cream to go along with it, sweet as sugar and thick enough to walk on. Now . . . about your coat . . ."

156

"It's finished?" Clancy asked, and Tippitt thought he looked somehow disappointed.

"Not so you'd notice," he replied. He took Clancy out and showed him the sparrow's nest.

"Aye, it's spring," Clancy said. "The hedge is in blossom and the birds are building. Let them be, Tippitt. Sure I've no need of the coat till winter, now, and you'll have it done by then."

"You're a reasonable man, Clance," Tippitt said, and Sam nodded — twice.

"Not all the time," Clancy said. "But a man learns. A garden comes back with care and attention. I thought maybe a friendship could too."

Tippitt smiled and put his arm around Clancy's shoulders. "You're right," he said. "Now wasn't it the luckiest thing, Clance, that your old coat needed turning?"

Clancy winked. "I told you there was a lot of use left in it."

Tippitt chuckled. "Well, I'll be jakered!"

The New All-Purpose Coat

Tippitt never got around to
repairing Clancy's coat because he
kept finding other uses for the coat.
Write an advertisement for a
coat like Clancy's, telling customers
about the many special ways the coat
can be used. Think of some new
uses for the coat, in addition to
Tippitt's uses in the story.

Make Friends

Christine McDonnell's ideas for stories come from her own memories of growing up in a town just like the one Leo, Ivy, and Emily live in.

McDonnell and son, Doo Wook.

Most of the stories in her books really happened. In elementary school, Christine McDonnell taught herself how to make origami figures by reading a library book.

She still remembers making a crane that would flap its wings when she pulled the tail.

McDonnell with daughter Soo Ae, son Garth, and husband Terry Shaneyfelt.

Karen Hirsch is both a teacher and a writer. She has taught in the public schools of Wisconsin since 1963. She has also spent a year teaching in Switzerland.

Hirsch and friend in their yard at home.

160

with These Authors

Karen Hirsch published her first book for young people in 1977. She has written a number of other books as well as articles for newspapers and children's magazines.

Karen Hirsch with her husband Tim Hirsch.

Bunting in Anchorage, Alaska.

Eve Bunting now lives in California, although she grew up in Ireland, where she knew a tailor very much like Tippitt. He made clothes, but never on time! Real-life people and events give Bunting the basic ideas for her stories. To these ideas she adds "imagination, hard work, and a lot of love."

Eve Bunting has written many books. Two you may enjoy are *Barney the Beard* and *Goose Dinner*.

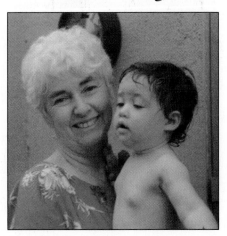

Eve Bunting with her granddaughter, Anna Eve.

Take a Friend to the Park

Lucky Charms & Birthday Wishes
by Christine McDonnell
Shy Emily meets Leo and Ivy in her new
class. With the help of her new friends,
Emily may indeed
have a good year.

Maude and Sally
by Nicki Weiss
Maude and Sally are best friends.
When Sally goes away to camp their
friendship changes over the summer.

162

Say "Cheese"
by Patricia Reilly Giff
Here is an adventure about a girl named
Emily and her search for a best friend
among the kids at the Polk Street School.

My Friend Jacob
by Lucille Clifton
Sam's best friend is Jacob,
a sixteen-year-old who is
mentally disabled. Each
boy shares a special skill
to help out the other.

Best Enemies
by Kathleen Leverich
Priscilla hopes to meet new friends as
school starts. Is a girl who plays tricks
on her a friend or an enemy?

163

BOOK 4

BEWARE! TROUBLE AHEAD

BEWARE OF

THE GLUMP!

BEWARE OF

MICE EATERS!

BEWARE OF DOG HATERS!

THE
CHARACTERS
YOU WILL MEET IN
THIS BOOK ALL HAVE GOOD
REASON TO PAY ATTENTION
TO WARNING SIGNS. READ
THESE STORIES
TO FIND OUT
WHY.

CONTENTS

Doctor De Soto 168
written and illustrated by William Steig

Beware of the Glump 180
by Virginia Bradley

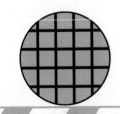

The Garden of Abdul Gasazi 192
written and illustrated by Chris Van Allsburg

CAUTION

167

Doctor De Soto

story and pictures by William Steig

Doctor De Soto, the dentist, did very good work, so he had no end of patients. Those close to his own size — moles, chipmunks, et cetera — sat in the regular dentist's chair.

Larger animals sat on the floor, while Doctor De Soto stood on a ladder.

For extra-large animals, he had a special room. There Doctor De Soto was hoisted up to the patient's mouth by his assistant, who also happened to be his wife.

Doctor De Soto was especially popular with the big animals. He was able to work inside their mouths, wearing rubbers to keep his feet dry; and his fingers were so delicate, and his drill so dainty, they could hardly feel any pain.

Being a mouse, he refused to treat animals dangerous to mice, and it said so on his sign. When the doorbell rang, he and his wife would look out the window. They wouldn't admit even the most timid-looking cat.

One day, when they looked out, they saw a well-dressed fox with a flannel bandage around his jaw.

"I cannot treat you, sir!" Doctor De Soto shouted. "Sir! Haven't you read my sign?"

"Please!" the fox wailed. "Have mercy, I'm suffering!" And he wept so bitterly it was pitiful to see.

"Just a moment," said Doctor De Soto. "That poor fox," he whispered to his wife. "What shall we do?"

"Let's risk it," said Mrs. De Soto. She pressed the buzzer and let the fox in.

He was up the stairs in a flash. "Bless your little hearts," he cried, falling to his knees. "I beg you, *do* something! My tooth is killing me."

"Sit on the floor, sir," said Doctor De Soto, "and remove the bandage, please."

Doctor De Soto climbed up the ladder and bravely entered the fox's mouth. "Ooo-wow!" he gasped. The fox had a rotten bicuspid and unusually bad breath.

"This tooth will have to come out," Doctor De Soto announced. "But we can make you a new one."

"Just stop the pain," whimpered the fox, wiping some tears away.

Despite his misery, he realized he had a tasty little morsel in his mouth, and his jaw began to quiver. "Keep open!" yelled Doctor De Soto. "Wide open!" yelled his wife.

"I'm giving you gas now," said Doctor De Soto. "You won't feel a thing when I yank that tooth."

Soon the fox was in dreamland. "M-m-m, yummy," he mumbled. "How I love them raw . . . with just a pinch of salt. . . ."

They could guess what he was dreaming about. Mrs. De Soto handed her husband a pole to keep the fox's mouth open.

Doctor De Soto fastened his extractor to the bad tooth. Then he and his wife began turning the winch.

Finally, with a sucking sound, the tooth popped out and hung swaying in the air.

"I'm bleeding!" the fox yelped when he came to.

Doctor De Soto ran up the ladder and stuffed some gauze in the hole. "The worst is over," he said. "I'll have your new tooth ready tomorrow. Be here at eleven sharp."

The fox, still woozy, said goodbye and left. On his way home, he wondered if it would be shabby of him to eat the De Sotos when the job was done.

After office hours, Mrs. De Soto molded a tooth of pure gold and polished it. "Raw with salt, indeed," muttered Doctor De Soto. "How foolish to trust a fox!"

"He didn't know what he was saying," said Mrs. De Soto. "Why should he harm us? We're helping him."

"Because he's a fox!" said Doctor De Soto. "They're wicked, wicked creatures."

That night the De Sotos lay awake worrying. "Should we let him in tomorrow?" Mrs. De Soto wondered.

"Once I start a job," said the dentist firmly, "I finish it. My father was the same way."

"But we must do something to protect ourselves," said his wife. They talked and talked until they formed a plan. "I think it will work," said Doctor De Soto. A minute later he was snoring.

The next morning, promptly at eleven, a very cheerful fox turned up. He was feeling not a particle of pain.

When Doctor De Soto got into his mouth, he snapped it shut for a moment, then opened wide and laughed. "Just a joke!" he chortled.

"Be serious," said the dentist sharply. "We have work to do." His wife was lugging the heavy tooth up the ladder.

"Oh, I love it!" exclaimed the fox. "It's just beautiful."

Doctor De Soto set the gold tooth in its socket and hooked it up to the teeth on both sides.

The fox caressed the new tooth with his tongue. "My, it feels good," he thought. "I really shouldn't eat them. On the other hand, how can I resist?"

"We're not finished," said Doctor De Soto, holding up a large jug. "I have here a remarkable preparation developed only recently by my wife and me. With just one application, you can be rid of toothaches forever. How would you like to be the first one to receive this unique treatment?"

"I certainly would!" the fox declared. "I'd be honored." He hated any kind of personal pain.

"You will never have to see us again," said Doctor De Soto.

"*No one* will see you again," said the fox to himself. He had definitely made up his mind to eat them — with the help of his brand-new tooth.

Doctor De Soto stepped into the fox's mouth with a bucket of secret formula and proceeded to paint each tooth. He hummed as he worked. Mrs. De Soto stood by on the ladder, pointing out spots he had missed. The fox looked very happy.

When the dentist was done, he stepped out. "Now close your jaws tight," he said, "and keep them closed for a full minute." The fox did as he was told. Then he tried to open his mouth — but his teeth were stuck together!

"Ah, excuse me, I should have mentioned," said Doctor De Soto, "you won't be able to open your mouth for a day or two. The secret formula must first permeate the dentine. But don't worry. No pain ever again!"

The fox was stunned. He stared at Doctor De Soto, then at his wife. They smiled, and waited. All he could do was say, "Frank oo berry mush" through his clenched teeth, and get up and leave. He tried to do so with dignity.

Then he stumbled down the stairs in a daze. Doctor De Soto and his assistant had outfoxed the fox. They kissed each other and took the rest of the day off.

Dangerous Patients

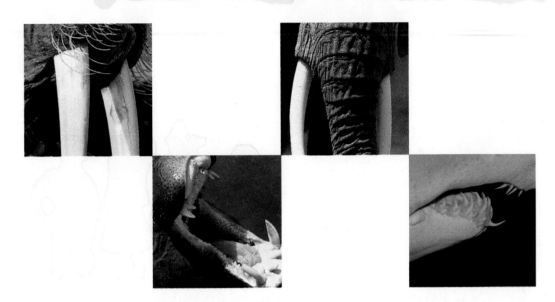

Most dentists keep records of all of their patients. Write a report about Doctor De Soto's most dangerous patient yet, the fox. Include in the report the patient's problems, behavior, and any other unusual facts. Be sure to suggest your ideas for the best treatment for the fox.

Beware of

The Narrator

The Children of the Town

The Woman
of the Town

The Man
of the Town

The Mayor
of the Town

The Stranger

C. Q. Glump, Esquire

The Glump

A Puppet Play by Virginia Bradley
Illustrated by Shannon Kriegshauser

The NARRATOR *comes out to stand at the side of the puppet theater and speaks to the audience.*

NARRATOR: Once upon a time there was a town called Sidnitz. And there in the town, down by the river road, there lived a man named Glump. C. Q. Glump. At least I'm quite sure he lived there. No one ever went to see him. You see, everyone was afraid of the glump. That's what they called him . . . the glump. Certainly all the children had strict instructions to stay away from the river road. In fact, they used to chant the warning all the way to school in the morning.

(Curtain opens on a street in the town. There is a backdrop of buildings and at the left end there is a sign: THE MAYOR. *Attached to the sign is a little bell. The* CHILDREN *enter right and go across the stage chanting, "Stay away from the river road . . . stay away from the river road." They exit left.)*

NARRATOR: And all the way home. *(*CHILDREN *enter left and go back across the stage chanting, "The glump, the glump . . . Beware of the glump." They exit right as the* NARRATOR *continues.)* No one ever knew why the people were afraid. No one ever talked about it. Then one day a stranger came to town. He had business with C. Q. Glump, and he started to inquire around . . . well, just listen . . .

(The STRANGER *enters from the right. He wears a long coat and a black drooping-brimmed hat. The* WOMAN *of the town enters from the left and they meet.)*

STRANGER: Good morning, madam. Can you tell me where I will find a Mr. Glump?

WOMAN: *Who* did you say?

STRANGER: Mr. Glump, madam. C. Q. Glump.
I have business with him.

WOMAN: Oh dear me, I was afraid you'd said
glump. I tell you, stranger, they say the
glump lives down by the river road, but I
shouldn't go there if I were you.

STRANGER: And why shouldn't I?

WOMAN: The glump is a terrible creature. *(She
comes close to the* STRANGER *and whispers.)*
I've only seen him once and that was
enough. He has this enormous nose . . . Oh
dear, I've talked too much already. You'll
have to excuse me. *(She exits left.)*

STRANGER *(calls after her)*: But madam, you
have . . . *(He realizes she is out of earshot. He
turns and mumbles to himself.)* Enormous
nose, indeed. I'll just have to ask someone
else. *(He moves slowly toward the exit right.)*

NARRATOR: Well, the stranger was a little
perplexed, but just then a man of the town
came along the street. (MAN *enters right.*)

MAN: You seem to be a stranger, mister. Can I
do something for you?

STRANGER: Perhaps you can, sir. Which way
do I go to get to the river road?

MAN: The river road!

STRANGER: Yes. I understand Mr. Glump lives
down that way. I have business with him.

MAN: With the glump? What possible business
could you have with the glump?

STRANGER: That's my business, sir. Can you
direct me?

MAN: I wouldn't direct my worst enemy to the river road, mister. The glump is a frightful creature.

STRANGER: But why is he so frightful? An enormous nose is nothing to be afraid of.

MAN: Oh, it's not his nose, mister. It's his . . . *(he hesitates)* Well, I might as well tell you, although I've not spoken of it to a living soul. He has these huge floppy ears . . . frightful, mister, frightful. No, I wouldn't direct you, mister. Forget it. Just forget it. *(He scurries off to the right leaving the* STRANGER *calling after him.)*

STRANGER: But come back, sir. Don't you know that . . .

NARRATOR: Well, the stranger was getting a little impatient. Then he noticed that right there on the street was the office of the mayor of the town. He went up and rang the little bell which hung above the door. *(The* STRANGER *has moved to the left end of the street. He rings the bell, and the* MAYOR *emerges.)*

STRANGER: Your honor, you are the mayor of Sidnitz?

MAYOR: I am indeed. What can I do for you, stranger?

STRANGER: I have been trying to get directions to the river road. I want to see Mr. Glump.

MAYOR: Well, now that's an unfortunate request, stranger.

STRANGER: But why? I have business with Mr. Glump. Won't you tell me how to get to his house?

MAYOR: Couldn't do it, stranger . . . just couldn't do it. As mayor of the town, I must think of its reputation. If I told you the way to the river road, you might . . . no, no, I'm afraid I couldn't direct you to the glump.

STRANGER: I know everyone seems to think he is a terrible, frightful creature. But I'm not afraid of an enormous nose and floppy ears. That's foolish.

MAYOR: What do you mean . . . *nose* and *ears*? If I were to tell you . . . yes, I can see you're a stubborn fellow. Come closer. *(He pulls the STRANGER to him and talks in an urgent voice.)* The glump is indeed a dreadful creature. It's his eyebrows . . . his thick shaggy eyebrows.

STRANGER: But your honor . . .

MAYOR *(interrupting)*: That's all I will say, and don't you tell anyone I discussed this with you, or I might not win the election next week. *(MAYOR looks to the right and left before he exits the way he came.)*

STRANGER (*to himself*): There are certainly strange people in this town. Well, I'm not afraid of shaggy eyebrows either. I'll just find the river road by myself. (*He exits left as the curtain closes.*)

NARRATOR: The stranger was indeed baffled, but he was determined to find Mr. Glump. He walked on past the post office and the library and down beyond the cemetery to the river road. There ahead of him he saw Glump's gate.

(*Curtain opens and the* STRANGER *enters from the right. At the far left is a white picket fence with a sign on it:* C. Q. GLUMP, ESQUIRE.)

STRANGER (*goes to the gate and calls out*): Sir! Mr. Glump, sir. I would like to talk to you.

MR. GLUMP (*offstage*): To me! No one ever talks to me. I'll be right there.

(MR. GLUMP *enters from the left. He has an enormous nose, huge floppy ears, thick shaggy eyebrows, and a shock of red hair which stands straight up in the air.*)

MR. GLUMP: I am delighted, simply delighted.
What can I do for you, sir? (*The* STRANGER
*gives a great yelp and runs off right,
leaving* MR. GLUMP *shaking his head in
bewilderment.*) Now what in the world is the
matter with him? (*Quick curtain.*)

NARRATOR: Well, the stranger made his way
back to town. Past the cemetery, past the
library, past the post office. And there on
the main street he bumped right into the
mayor who was talking to the man and the
woman of the town.

WOMAN: I see you found out the glump *is*
  terrible with an enormous nose. I told you.

MAN: You wouldn't listen when I warned you of
  his huge floppy ears. Frightful.

MAYOR: Dreadful. With his . . . *(The* MAYOR
  starts to say "with his thick shaggy eyebrows"
  and then he stops himself.)

STRANGER: Oh, those things didn't bother me
  at all. What bothered me was his hair.
  Horrible. Horrible. I think I may faint.
  (The STRANGER *takes off his black drooping*
  hat to fan himself and reveals a great shock of
  red hair which stands straight up in the air.)

  (Quick curtain.)

NARRATOR *(Calls the* PUPPETEERS *out for*
  introductions. When he has finished, he has a
  final word.): Funny thing. No one ever did
  find out what the
  stranger's business was.

Create a New Glump

The glump in the play had these unusual features:

- an enormous nose
- huge floppy ears
- thick shaggy eyebrows
- and a shock of red hair that stood straight up in the air

Create a brand-new glump. On a sheet of paper, list the glump's "new" features. Then tell a different version of the play to a friend based on what the new glump looks like. Remember, the other characters will each have to look like the glump in one particular way.

THE GARDEN OF ABDUL GASAZI

written and illustrated
by Chris Van Allsburg

Six times Miss Hester's dog Fritz
had bitten dear cousin Eunice. So when
Miss Hester received an invitation to visit
Eunice she was not surprised to read
"P.S., Please leave your dog home."
On the day of her visit Miss Hester
asked young Alan Mitz to stay with Fritz
and give him his afternoon walk.

As soon as Miss Hester left, Fritz ran into the parlor. He loved to chew on the chairs and shake the stuffing out of the pillows. But Alan was ready. All morning long he kept Fritz from sinking his sharp little teeth into the furniture. Finally the dog gave up and fell asleep, exhausted. Alan took a nap, too, but first he hid his hat under his shirt, hats being one of Fritz's favorite things to chew.

An hour later Alan quickly awoke when Fritz gave him a bite on the nose. The bad-mannered dog was ready for his afternoon walk. Alan fastened Fritz's leash and the dog dragged him out of the house.

Walking along, they discovered a small white bridge at the side of the road. Alan decided to let Fritz lead the way across.

Some distance beyond the bridge Alan stopped to read a sign. It said: ABSOLUTELY, POSITIVELY NO DOGS ALLOWED IN THIS GARDEN. At the bottom it was signed: ABDUL GASAZI, RETIRED MAGICIAN. Behind the sign stood a vine-covered wall with an open doorway. Alan took the warning quite seriously. He turned to leave, but as he did, Fritz gave a tremendous tug and snapped right out of his collar. He bolted straight ahead through the open door, with Alan running right behind.

"Fritz, stop, you bad dog!" cried Alan, but the dog simply ignored him.

Down shadowed paths and across sunlit lawns they

raced, deeper and deeper into the garden. Finally, Alan drew close enough to grab hold of Fritz. But as he reached out he slipped and fell. Fritz barked with laughter as he galloped out of sight. Alan slowly picked himself up. He knew he had to find Fritz before Mr. Gasazi discovered him. Bruised and tired, he hurried off in the dog's direction.

After a long search Alan was ready to give up. He was afraid he might never find Fritz. But then he came upon fresh dog prints. Slowly he followed Fritz's tracks along a path that led into a forest. The dirt path ended and a brick wall began. There were no more tracks to follow, but Alan was certain that Fritz must be just ahead.

Alan started running. In front of him he could see a clearing in the forest. As he came dashing out of the

woods he stopped as quickly as if he had run up against a wall. For there, in front of him, stood a truly awesome sight. It was the house of Gasazi. Alan nervously climbed the great stairs, convinced Fritz had come this way and been captured.

The boy's heart was pounding when he arrived at the huge door. He took a deep breath and reached for the bell, but before he touched it the door swung open. There, in the shadow of the hallway, stood Gasazi the Great. "Greetings, do come in" was all that he said.

Alan followed Gasazi into a large room. When the magician turned around Alan quickly apologized for letting Fritz into the garden. He politely asked that, if Mr. Gasazi had Fritz, would he please give him back?

The magician listened carefully and then, smiling, said, "Certainly you may have your little Fritzie. Follow me." With those words he went to the door and led Alan back outside.

They were walking across the lawn when suddenly Gasazi stopped by a gathering of ducks. He began to speak in a voice that was more like a growl. "I detest dogs. They dig up my flowers, they chew on my trees. Do you know what I do to dogs I find in my garden?"

"What?" whispered Alan, almost afraid to hear the answer.

"I TURN THEM INTO DUCKS!" bellowed Gasazi.

In horror, Alan looked at the birds in front of him. When one duck came forward, Gasazi said, "There's your Fritz."

Alan begged the magician to change Fritz

back. "Impossible," he answered, "only time can do that. This spell may last years or perhaps just a day. Now take your dear bird and please don't come again."

When Alan took the bird in his arms it tried to give him a bite. "Good old boy," said Alan sadly as he patted the bird on the head. "You really haven't changed so much." With tears in his eyes he started for home. Behind him Alan could hear Gasazi laughing. As he approached the stairway, a gust of wind took Alan's hat sailing right off his head. Running along with one arm reaching for the hat, Alan lost his hold on Fritz. The duck flew out ahead and grabbed the hat in midair. But instead of landing he just kept on flying, higher and higher, until he disappeared in the afternoon clouds.

Alan just stood and stared at the empty sky. "Goodbye, old fellow," he called out sadly, sure that Fritz was gone forever. At least he had something to chew on. Slowly, one step after another, Alan found his way back to the garden gate and over the bridge. It was sunset by the time he reached Miss Hester's. Lights were on and he knew she must be home. With a heavy heart he approached the door, wondering how Miss Hester would take the news.

When Miss Hester came to the door Alan blurted out his incredible story. He could barely hold back the tears; then, racing out of the kitchen, dog food on his nose, came Fritz. Alan couldn't believe his eyes.

"I'm afraid Mr. Gasazi played a trick on you," said Miss Hester, trying to hide a smile. "Fritz was in the

front yard when I returned. He must have found his own way home while you were with Mr. Gasazi. You see, Alan, no one can really turn dogs into ducks; that old magician just made you think that duck was Fritz."

Alan felt very silly. He promised himself he'd never be fooled like that again. He was too old to believe in magic. Miss Hester watched from the porch as Alan waved goodbye and hurried down the road to go home. Then she called out to Fritz, who was playfully running around the front yard. He came trotting up the front steps with something in his mouth and dropped it at Miss Hester's feet. "Why you bad dog," she said. "What are you doing with Alan's hat?"

HOW DID THAT HAT GET THERE?

How do you think Fritz got Alan's hat? Could Abdul Gasazi have actually changed Fritz into a duck? Think of an explanation for how the hat might have gotten into the front yard. Then discuss your explanation with your classmates. Try to convince them that your explanation is what really happened.

POETRY AHEAD

A WARNING ABOUT BEARS

Some bears are fierce, and most grow fiercer
When any one bites off their ears, sir.
With bears it's best to be polite.
And a bit distant — that's all right.
But, please, when meeting bears, don't bite.

MORE ABOUT BEARS

Some bears are fierce, and some are fiercer.
Few bears (I rather hope) are near, sir.
From what I know of bears, they are
Better few and better far.

STILL MORE ABOUT BEARS

The fiercest bear of all is very
(A good thing, too) imaginary.
I say "a good thing" for, my dear,
If he were real, he might be here.

LAST WORD ABOUT BEARS

I meet few bears and few meet me.
But still it's my belief
That, meeting bears, the thing to be
Is — brief.

John Ciardi

211

THE BLOATH

In the undergrowth
There dwells a Bloath
Who feeds upon poets and tea.
Luckily, I know this about him
While he knows almost nothing of me!

Shel Silverstein

Something is there

Something is there
    there on the stair
        coming down
            coming down
                stepping with care.
                    Coming down
                        coming down
                            slinkety-sly.

Something is coming and wants to get by.

Lilian Moore

AUTHORS

Chris Van Allsburg

Drawing was just a hobby for Chris Van Allsburg. But a friend who liked his work suggested he try to illustrate a book. So in his spare time, he did pencil drawings of a little boy, a dog, and a magician. The story became *The Garden of Abdul Gasazi*. Today Chris Van Allsburg is one of the most popular illustrator-authors in the history of children's literature. You might also enjoy reading his books *The Polar Express* and *Two Bad Ants*.

William Steig

William Steig began his career as a cartoonist. He sold his first drawing in the 1930's and since then has drawn for national magazines. When he was sixty-one years old he wrote his first children's book, *Roland the Minstrel Pig*. William Steig has written other books that you might enjoy reading, including *Amos & Boris,* about a mouse and a whale, and *Spinky Sulks,* about a boy who sulks all day.

Virginia Bradley

Virginia Bradley says she's always lived in the world of make-believe. As a girl, she would put on shows in her backyard for the people of her neighborhood. When she grew up she wrote plays for Cub Scouts, for Brownies, and for school functions. Many of the ideas for her books come from these performances.

STOP FOR THESE BOOKS

Lyle, Lyle, Crocodile
by BERNARD WABER

The Secret
in the
Matchbox
Val Willis
Pictures by
John Shelley

THE VINGANANEE AND THE TREE TOAD
RETOLD BY VERNA AARDEMA WITH ILLUSTRATIONS BY ELLEN WEISS
A LIBERIAN TALE

Lyle, Lyle, Crocodile *by Bernard Waber*

Lyle is a sweet, lovable crocodile. Why would anyone want him locked behind bars in a zoo?

The Vingananee and the Tree Toad: A Liberian Tale *by Verna Aardema*

Spider and his animal friends enjoy their farm life until the terrible Vingananee comes and eats their stew.

The Enormous Crocodile *by Roald Dahl*

Crocodile wants a nice juicy child for lunch. He tries every nasty trick he can think of to get one.

A Toad for Tuesday *by Russell Erickson*

Warton the toad becomes involved in a thrilling adventure when he is captured by a terrible owl.

Guys from Space *by Daniel Pinkwater*

Aliens land in a boy's backyard and invite him to visit a "neat planet" with them.

The Secret in the Matchbox *by Val Willis*

Bobby has a secret pet that he keeps in a matchbox. Bobby is in for big trouble when he brings his secret pet to school.

Glossary

Some of the words in this book may have pronunciations or meanings you do not know. This glossary can help you by telling you how to pronounce those words and by telling you the meanings with which those words are used in this book.

You can find out the correct pronunciation of any glossary word by using the special spelling after the word and the pronunciation key that runs across the bottom of the glossary pages.

The full pronunciation key opposite shows how to pronounce each consonant and vowel in a special spelling. The pronunciation key at the bottom of the glossary pages is a shortened form of the full key.

FULL PRONUNCIATION KEY

Consonant Sounds

b	bib	k	cat, kick, pique	th	path, thin
ch	church	l	lid, needle	*th*	bathe, this
d	deed	m	am, man, mum	v	cave, valve,
f	fast, fife, off,	n	no, sudden		vine
	phase, rough	ng	thing	w	with
g	gag	p	pop	y	yes
h	hat	r	roar	z	rose, size,
hw	which	s	miss, sauce, see		xylophone,
j	judge	sh	dish, ship		zebra
		t	tight	zh	garage,
					pleasure, vision

Vowel Sounds

ă	pat	î	dear, deer,	ou	cow, out
ā	aid, they, pay		fierce, mere	ŭ	cut, rough
â	air, care, wear	ŏ	pot, horrible	û	firm, heard,
ä	father	ō	go, row, toe		term, turn,
ĕ	pet, pleasure	ô	alter, caught,		word
ē	be, bee, easy,		for, paw	yōō	abuse, use
	seize	oi	boy, noise, oil	ə	about, silent,
ĭ	pit	o͞o	book		pencil, lemon,
ī	by, guy, pie	o͞o	boot		circus
				ər	butter

STRESS MARKS

Primary Stress ′	Secondary Stress ′
bi•ol•o•gy [bī ŏl′ə jē]	bi•o•log•i•cal [bī′ə lŏj′ĭ kəl]

ab•ra•ca•dab•ra
(ăb′rə kə **dăb**′rə) A word
once thought to have
magical powers: *Waving a
wand over the hat, the
magician cried,
"Abracadabra!"*

ab•so•lute•ly (ăb′sə **loot**′lē)
In truth; without a doubt.
ABSOLUTELY NO DOGS
ALLOWED IN THIS
GARDEN means that no
dogs could enter the garden
for any reason.

ad•mire (ăd **mīr**′) To look at
and think about with
pleasure or respect:
*Of all the people Tom
admires, the person he
most looks up to is
Martin Luther King, Jr.*

ap•pli•ca•tion (ăp′lĭ **kā**′shən)
The giving of medicine,
especially by prescription:
*The patient needed only
one application of medicine
to feel better.*

as•sis•tant (ə **sĭs**′tənt) A
person who helps out; a
helper: *The doctor's
assistant helped the doctor
by answering the phone.*

awe•some (ô′səm) Causing
feelings of wonder,
amazement, and fear: *The
astronaut's view of Earth
from the Moon was an
awesome sight.*

back•ing (băk′ĭng) A large
sheet of cloth to which the
patches of a quilt are sewn.

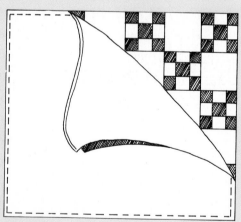

backing

baf•fled (băf′əld) Confused.
"The stranger was baffled"
means that the stranger did
not understand what was
going on.

ă pat / ā pay / â care / ä father / ĕ pet / ē be / ĭ pit / ī pie / î fierce / ŏ pot / ō go / ô paw, for /
oi oil / oo book /

bal·ance (băl′əns) To make something steady so that it does not fall: *Can you **balance** that card so it stands on its edge without tipping over?*

bi·cus·pid (bī kŭs′pĭd) A tooth with two points. An adult has eight bicuspids.

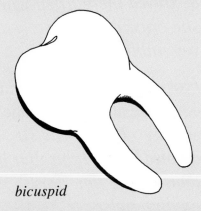

bicuspid

bind·ing (bīn′dĭng) The long cloth strip that holds the pages of a book together.

board·ing school (bôr′dĭng sko͞ol) A school at which students live during the school year: *When Sue went to **boarding school,** she lived in a room right across from the school library.*

book spine (bo͝ok spīn) The part of the book cover that joins the front and back covers.

brat·ty (brăt′tē) Not well-behaved: *The **bratty** children acted badly when they didn't get what they wanted.*

bri·dle (brīd′l) The straps, bit, and reins placed over a horse's head and used to guide and control the animal.

bridle

cap·ture (kăp′chər) To hold by force: *Alan was worried that Fritz had been **captured.***

chal·lenge (chăl′ənj) To demand that a person prove his or her ability: *Many people **challenged** Houdini to prove he really could escape.*

---

o͞o **boot** / ou **out** / ŭ **cut** / û **fur** / *th* **the** / th **thin** / hw **wh**ich / zh vision /
ə **ago, item, pencil, atom, circus**

chal•lenge (**chăl′**ənj) A task that is difficult or takes a lot of effort: *It was a **challenge** to make jam out of all the plums because there were so many of them.*

chop•sticks (**chŏp′**stĭks′) A pair of thin sticks used for eating, especially in Asian countries.

chopsticks

com•mand (kə **mănd′**) To direct; give orders to: *The magician **commanded** the man to crow like a rooster, and he did.*

com•pli•ment (**kŏm′**plə mənt′) To say something nice about someone.

con•vinced (kən **vĭnsd′**) Caused to do or to believe something; made certain: *Anne was **convinced** something had happened to her dog, Tippy, when he didn't answer to her call.*

D

deaf ed•u•ca•tion (dĕf ĕj′ə **kā′**shən) Instruction or classes for people who have hearing problems.

de•stroy (dĭ **stroi′**) To ruin completely: *The cow **destroyed** the garden when she crushed all the vegetables.*

de•vot•ed (dĭ **vō′**tĭd) Giving complete attention to one activity: *Pedro was so **devoted** to his tuba that he didn't have time for anything else.*

dread•ful (**drĕd′**fəl) Terrible; scary: *The mayor called the glump a **dreadful** creature because he thought the glump was ugly and frightening.*

E

e•nor•mous (ĭ **nôr′**məs) Very big; huge: *A cow is big, but an elephant is **enormous**.*

ă pat / ā pay / â care / ä father / ĕ pet / ē be / ĭ pit / ī pie / î fierce / ŏ pot / ō go / ô paw, for / oi oil / ŏŏ book /

es•cape (ĭ skāp′) The act of getting free or breaking loose: *To escape, Houdini freed himself from the ropes tied around his wrists.*

ex•pand your ho•ri•zons (ĭk spănd′; hə rī′zənz) Add to a person's experience or knowledge. When the librarian told Margaret "expand your horizons," she meant Margaret should learn new things by reading different kinds of books.

F

fab•ric (făb′rĭk) Cloth.

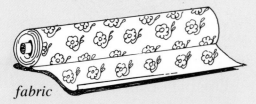

fabric

float•ing (flō′tĭng) Moving or resting in space without any support: *The princess was called the floating princess because she seemed to move through the air without having anything to hold her up.*

flop•py (flŏp′ē) Not stiff; moving back and forth or up and down in a clumsy way: *His ears were so floppy that they flapped like a flag in the wind.*

fright•ful (frīt′fəl) Terrible; awful: *A frightful creature is something to be afraid of.*

frus•tra•ted (frŭs′trāt ĭd) Feeling puzzled or helpless: *Emily felt frustrated because no matter how hard she tried, she couldn't make a crane out of the paper.*

G

gal•lop (găl′əp) The fast pace of a horse, having a quick three-beat rhythm: *When the horse started to gallop, the rider had to hold on tightly.*

gallop

oo b**oo**t / ou **out** / ŭ c**u**t / û f**u**r / *th* **th**e / th **th**in / hw **wh**ich / zh vi**s**ion /
ə **a**go, it**e**m, penc**i**l, at**o**m, circ**u**s

gas (găs) A substance that is neither solid nor liquid: *There is a special gas that makes hot-air balloons rise.*

gauze (gôz) A very thin, loosely connected cloth that is often used to cover a wound.

goof it up (goof ĭt ŭp) Spoil or ruin something by making careless mistakes. When the children said Becky was goofing it up, they meant she was ruining the game.

groom (groom) **1.** To clean, brush, feed, and take care of horses and other animals. **2.** The man at a wedding who is getting married.

hear·ing im·paired (hîr′ĭng ĭm pârd′) Unable to hear well. A program for the hearing impaired helps people who have trouble hearing or who are deaf.

hyp·no·tize (hĭp′nə tīz′) To put someone into a relaxed but alert kind of sleep: *The magician hypnotized someone from the audience by making that person relax.*

il·lus·tra·tion (ĭl′ə strā′shən) A picture, diagram, or chart used to explain or decorate: *The illustration showed how to do the magic trick.*

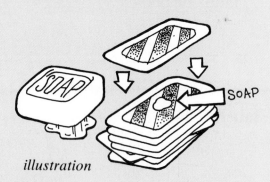

illustration

im·pa·tient (ĭm pā′shənt) Unable or unwilling to wait for something: *Nancy became impatient when she couldn't find anyone to give her directions.*

ă pat / ā pay / â care / ä father / ĕ pet / ē be / ĭ pit / ī pie / î fierce / ŏ pot / ō go / ô paw, for / oi oil / oo book /

in•sult (ĭn sŭlt′) To say something hurtful and mean; to behave in a rude manner: *The driver of the car insulted the man crossing the street by blowing his horn and yelling at him.*

INSULT

Years ago, insult meant "to leap upon someone or to attack suddenly."

---

man•ners (măn′ərz) Behavior toward others; ways of treating others: *You showed good manners when you offered your guest some tea.*

mar•vel (mär′vəl) Someone or something that causes surprise, astonishment, or wonder: *The crowd blinked with amazement at the marvel of the disappearing elephant.*

mas•ter•piece (măs′tər pēs′) An artist's greatest work. When Grandma said she was going to make a masterpiece, she meant that she was going to make the best quilt of her life.

MASTERPIECE

In the past, craftsmen presented their best work to a group of judges. If their work was good enough they would be called masters.

---

ma•te•ri•al (mə tîr′ē əl) Cloth: *The quilt was sewn from many different kinds of material.*

mid-air also **mid•air** (mĭd âr′) A point or region in the middle of the air: *When the balloon rose halfway to the ceiling, it was floating in mid-air.*

mir•a•cle (mĭr′ə kəl) An event that seems impossible because it cannot be explained: *Some magic tricks seem like miracles because people do not know how they are done.*

ōō b**oo**t / ou **ou**t / ŭ c**u**t / û f**ur** / *th* **the** / th **thin** / hw **which** / zh vi**si**on /
ə **a**go, it**e**m, penc**i**l, at**o**m, circ**u**s

mount (mount) **1.** To get up on a horse or other animal. **2.** To put something in place, like a picture on a wall. **3.** To climb.

o•bliged (ə blījd′) Thankful: *A person who is **obliged** is thankful for something that has been said or done.*

pad•dock (păd′ək) A fenced-in field where horses are kept.

paddock

patch•work (păch′wûrk′) Pieces of cloth of many different colors, shapes, and sizes sewn together.

pa•tient (pā′shənt) A person who gets treatment from a doctor: *I am a **patient** of the new doctor who just moved to town.*

pat•tern (păt′ərn) A special design that is repeated over and over: *The pieces of cloth were arranged in a special **pattern** of stars and stripes.*

per•me•ate (pûr′mē āt′) To pass through and spread throughout: *The medicine had to **permeate** the whole tooth to work.*

per•plexed (pər plĕkst′) Confused: *If someone is **perplexed**, that person doesn't know what is going on.*

plum (plŭm) A small fruit with red, purple, or yellow skin.

poof (po͞of) A word used to show that something has disappeared: *Suddenly — **poof!** — the penny was gone.*

ă pat / ā pay / â care / ä father / ĕ pet / ē be / ĭ pit / ī pie / î fierce / ŏ pot / ō go / ô paw, for / oi oil / o͞o book /

pos•i•tive•ly (pŏz′ĭ tĭv lē)
Having no doubts.
"Positively no dogs
allowed in the garden"
means no dogs can enter
the garden at all.

pres•to (prĕs′tō) A word
magicians use for sudden
surprise: *The magician
said "Presto!" and a
rabbit jumped out of
the hat.*

quilt (kwĭlt) A bed covering
made by sewing together
two layers of material with
an inner layer of cotton,
wool, down, or feathers.

quilt

QUILT

At one time, quilt meant a "sack
filled with feathers." Today, some
quilts are still filled with feathers.

---

rear (rîr) To rise up on the
back legs: *If a horse is
rearing up, the horse is
standing on its back legs.*

rea•son•a•ble (rē′zə nə bəl)
Showing good sense; wise.
"A reasonable price" means
a price that seems fair.

re•hearse (rĭ hûrs′) To
practice in order to prepare
for a performance: *To be
sure he was ready for the
show, Houdini rehearsed
his magic tricks many
times.*

re•tired (rĭ tīrd′) Gave up
one's work, usually after
reaching a certain age:
*When the police officer
said he was retired, he
meant he no longer
worked as a police officer.*

ripe (rīp) Fully grown:
*Mr. Castle threw out the
small green plums and
used only the large, ripe
ones to make jam.*

risk (rĭsk) To take a chance.

---

o͞o **boot** / ou **out** / ŭ **cut** / û **fur** / *th* **the** / th **thin** / hw **which** / zh **vision** /
ə **ago**, **item**, **pencil**, **atom**, **circus**

rot•ten (rŏt′n) Very bad, decayed: *The tooth was so* **rotten** *it had to be pulled.*

---

saun•ter (sôn′tər) To walk in a slow, relaxed way: *The boy* **sauntered** *down the street because he was not in a hurry.*

se•ri•ous•ly (sîr′ē əs lē) Not joking or fooling: *It's hard to take Sarah* **seriously** *because she is always acting silly.*

shag•gy (shăg′ē) Having long, rough hair.

shaggy

show•off also **show-off** (shō′ôf′) Someone who tries to get attention by making his or her abilities noticed: *The* **showoff** *liked people to notice all the fancy things he could do with his eyes closed.*

sign (sīn) **1.** To use a language made up of hand motions instead of speech: *Becky couldn't hear, so she* **signed** *to tell what she meant.* **2.** To write your name, usually on an official paper. **3.** A board or poster that tells information.

spell (spĕl) **1.** A word or group of words thought to have magic power: *When Abdul Gasazi cast a* **spell** *on Fritz, he changed the dog into a duck.* **2.** To name or write the letters that form a word in the correct order.

stitch (stĭch) One complete movement of a threaded needle into and out of material in sewing: *Mother used tiny* **stitches** *to sew the hem in my dress.*

stitch

ă pat / ā pay / â care / ä father / ĕ pet / ē be / ĭ pit / ī pie / î fierce / ŏ pot / ō go / ô paw, for / oi oil / o͝o book /

stub·born (stŭb′ərn)
Refusing to change an idea
or purpose even though
others want you to change:
*When the mayor said the
stranger was **stubborn,** he
meant that the stranger
wouldn't change his mind.*

stunt (stŭnt) An act that
shows unusual skill and
bravery: *The rider
performed many
dangerous **stunts** such
as jumping onto the back
of a galloping horse.*

stunt

tex·ture (tĕks′chər) The feel
of something: *No two
patches of cloth had the
same **texture.** Some felt
soft, others felt rough.*

treat (trēt) To try to cure; to
give medical help: *The
doctor tried to **treat** the
patient's toothache.*

treat·ment (trēt′mənt) The
use of something to cure a
disease: *The doctor gave
the boy some medicine as
a **treatment** for his illness.*

trot (trŏt) To run slowly:
*The horses **trotted** around
the ring so that the judges
of the horse show could
look carefully at them.*

up·roar (ŭp′rôr′) Noisy
excitement and confusion:
*The principal's
announcement that classes
were canceled because of
the snow caused an **uproar**
in every class.*

van·ish (văn′ĭsh) To
disappear; become invisible:
*The elephant **vanished** and
was never seen again.*

---

o͞o boot / ou **out** / ŭ **cut** / û f**ur** / *th* **the** / th **thin** / hw **which** / zh **vision** /
ə **ago,** it**em,** penc**il,** at**om,** circ**us**